The role of cost saving and innovation in PFI projects

Construction Industry Council

Construction Industry Council

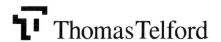

Published for the Construction Industry Council by Thomas Telford Publishing,

Thomas Telford Ltd, 1 Heron Quay, London E14 4JD.

URL: www.t-telford.com

Distributors for Thomas Telford books are

USA: ASCE Press 1801 Alexander Bell Drive. Reston, VA 20191-4400

Japan: Maruzen Co. Ltd, Book Department, 3–10 Nihonbashi 2-chome, Chuo-ku, Tokyo 103

Australia: DA Books and Journals, 648 Whitehorse Road, Mitcham 3132, Victoria

First published 2000

A catalogue record for this book is available from the British Library

ISBN: 0 7277 2879 2

Typeset by Rob Norridge

Printed and bound in Great Britain by Hobbs The Printers, Hampshire

Preface

In the last two years some £4bn to £5bn worth of deals have been signed and the provision of services through the Private Finance Initiative is now attaining a sense of permanence as a form of procurement. The construction industry is a major player in enabling the provision of these services. The Construction Industry Council recognised this and with financial help from the DETR commissioned Graham Ive and Andrew Edkins of the Bartlett to compile the *Constructors Key Guide to PFI*, which was published prior to this expansion.

As PFI matures, inevitably questions are being asked about its value for money and more particularly the role of cost saving and innovation. This publication, again commissioned by the CIC with financial help from the DETR, seeks to answer those questions. The authors of the previous publication, building on their knowledge and with the help of Germán Millán have looked at a number of case studies. In order to make better use of the findings there is an explanation of the nature of efficiency gains, the value of risk transfer and the inhibitors and enablers of innovation. The studies cover the healthcare, custodial and road sectors and the analysis is wide ranging, identifying the factors that affect the extent of cost saving and the nature of the innovations. Numerous charts provide the detail.

The conclusions and recommendations are helpful and important for all those involved in PFI from procurers in the Government to the operators and constructors in the private sector.

Herb Nahapiet OBE

Chairman, Construction Industry Council Private Finance Advisory Panel
Visiting Professor, The Bartlett, University College London
Managing Director, UKDS

Acknowledgements

To complete research of this kind, academic researchers need the assistance, patience, co-operation, and active collaboration of many practitioners.

The authors wish to thank the very many individuals who helped answer our questions, including our comprehensive survey, and solve our problems. We regret that it is not possible to thank you all by name.

We wish to acknowledge particularly the contributions of the following. Members of PFI / PPP Units of several Public Agencies, and among them, Neil Roden, Robert Hatcher and Tim Pope (Highways Agency), David Kent and Malcolm Lyon (HM Prison Service), Stephen Burt (DfEE), John Cryer and Heather Goldstraw (MoD), Andrew Lloyd-Kendall (NHS Executive) and David Wright (Funding Agency for Schools).

We would also like to thank Dick Wilkinson (Halcrow Group), John Carr and Nasser Massoud (Pricewaterhouse Coopers), Ian Hogdson (Denton Hall), John Thornely and Roger McGlynn (WS Atkins), Declan Gaffney (School of Social Policy, UCL) and Herb Nahapiet (UKDS) for their contributions during the early stages of the project.

We are very grateful to Roger McLachrie (Greater Manchester Fire and Civil Defence Authority), David Croft (Carden Croft & Co), Keith Heggarty (Snape Ltd.), Colin Kerr and Nuala Withey (Greenwich Healthcare NHS Trust), Peter Kane and Amir Quereshi (Kvaerner Construction), Chris Parker (Kingston-upon-Hull Local Education Authority), Paul Sewell and Graham Atkins (Sewell Group), Will Jones (VA Architecture) and Ian Renhard (Tilbury Douglas) for their help in the study of specific projects.

In providing the invaluable editorial assistance necessary to produce a report of this complexity we are indebted to the Members of the Research Steering Group for their specific help. In addition to members already mentioned above, we thank Adrian Jackson-Robbins and Martin Lockwood (Davis Langdon Consultancy), Tim Wilson (HM Treasury Private Finance Taskforce), Martin Lipson (4Ps), Dermot O'Reilly (TPS Consult), David Clements (WS Atkins) and Graham Watts, John Mead and Yiannis Koutsikidis (Construction Industry Council)

Finally, for their help on particular issues associated with this report, we would like to express our gratitude to Peter Lansley (University of Reading) and Phillip Cunliffe (*PFI Journal*).

Graham Ive
Andrew Edkins
Germán Millán
The Bartlett
UCL

Table of contents

Acronyms

4Ps	Public Private Partnerships Programme
BAFO	best and final offer
BOOT	build, own, operate and transfer
CSI(s)	cost saving innovation(s)
D&B	design and build contract
DBFO	design, build, finance and operate – see also PFI
DBO	design, build and operate
DCMF	design construct, manage and finance – see also PFI
DETR	Department of Environment, Transport and the Regions
DfEE	Department for Education and Employment
DoH	Department of Health
DSS	Department of Social Security
DTI	Department of Trade and Industry
FBC	full business case
FCO	Foreign & Commonwealth Office
FM	facilities management
GDH	Greenwich District Hospital
GMF&CDA	Greater Manchester Fire and Civil Defence Authority
HMPS	Her Majesty's Prison Service
HMSO	formerly HM Stationery Office, now The Stationery Office
HO	Home Office
ITN	invitation to negotiate
LA	local authorities
LCD	Lord Chancellor's Department
M&E	mechanical and electrical engineering
MoD	Ministry of Defence
NAO	National Audit Office
NHS	National Health Service
NI	Northern Ireland Office
NPC	net present cost
NPV	net present value
OBC	outline business case
OJEC	Official Journal of the European Community
OS	output specifications
PACS	picture archiving and communications system (IT system in new Queen Elizabeth PFI Hospital)
PFI	Private Finance Initiative – used referring both to the specific public policy with that name and as a generic term, also known by names such as PPP, DBFO, DCMF, BOOT and Concession
PFPE	Private Finance Panel Executive
PPP	Public Private Partnership – see also PFI
PRIME	Private Sector Resource Initiative for the Management of the Estate, from the DSS
PSC	public sector comparator
QEH	Queen Elizabeth Hospital
QEMH	Queen Elizabeth Military Hospital
R&D	research and development
RAF	Royal Air Force
SO	Scottish Office
SPV	special purpose vehicle – term used, within this text, to refer to a PFI company
TFO	traditionally funded option
TTF	HM Treasury PFI Taskforce
VFM	value for money
VFMC	value for money comparator
WO	Welsh Office

Glossary

Analysis of Difference: Test of null-hypothesis of no significance of difference between the median values of two different groups, or of one group and of the population from which those groups are drawn.

Analysis of Variance: Chi-squared test of null-hypothesis of no significance of variance between the distributions of groups and the distribution of the population from which those groups are drawn. Used in Chapter Four.

Ancillary Services: Services included in the PFI contract, which do not constitute core operations for the provision of the service to the final user.

Asset Specificity: The extent to which a transaction is supported by 'investments' or expenditures whose value depends upon continuance or completion of that specific transaction. After a contract is signed, the extent of asset specificity may be thought of as the cost to either party of replacing the other.

Awarding Authority: Public sector legal entity that contracts with the private sector for the purpose of procuring the PFI service.

Boundedly Rational Search: Human agents are subject to bounded rationality where behaviour is 'intendedly rational, but only limitedly so'. These limitations include the costs of searching for an optimum. As a result, a boundedly-rational search may conclude when a satisfactory, rather than optimum, solution is found.

Capital Cost: Cost arising from the initial Investment required by the PFI contract.

Capital Cost Saving: Costs can be divided into initial, or capital, costs and subsequent, or operating, costs. A capital cost saving represents a reduction in initial or pre-operational expenditure and thus a reduction in the amount of initial capital finance (equity capital or borrowing) required. See also 'Operational Cost Saving'

Centralised Client: Centralised Agency of the Government with substantial previous experience of procurement of similar facilities, and of PFI services. See Section A.5.2, p.118.

Client Adviser: Public sector clients for PFI project usually engage private firms to provide them with specialist and specific technical, legal and financial advice in relation to the project. These firms are called client advisers.

Clinical Services: Core operations of healthcare sector. They are usually outside the scope of the PFI healthcare contracts.

Complete Contracts: See Section 2.5, p.17.

Contractor: Used here in its conventional construction industry usage, to describe the firm that undertakes to execute a construction contract for a client. In the PFI context, the client of the contractor is the SPV or the PFI Company.

Conventionally Funded Solution: Alternative solution to the PFI route, which might have been financed through the traditional sources of public funding, instead of the private investment required by a PFI contract.

Core operations: Operations that constitute the principal activities of a public service organisation or business. E.g. custodial services in a prison, and clinical services in a hospital.

Cost Saving: In the context of this report, usually a percentage difference between estimates of cost for a PFI project and benchmark estimates for the project.

Cost Saving Innovation: Innovation that implies a reduction in costs, through cost saving solutions, whilst leaving the value of the product or service unchanged. See Section 2.3, p.11.

Decentralised Client: Agency of the Government without substantial recent experience of procurement of similar facilities or PFI services. See Section A.5.2, p.118.

Degrees of Potential Surprise: See Section 2.2, p.8.

Designer: Used here in its conventional construction industry usage, to describe the firm that undertakes to develop a client's specification and brief into a design, which then becomes the basis for a construction contract. This may be a design for a whole project or for part of a project. See also Principal Designer. In the PFI context, the client of the designer is the SPV or the PFI company.

Facilities Management (FM): Process by which an organisation delivers and sustains agreed levels of support service in a built environment facility, to meet the business need of the occupier of that facility. Support or ancillary services included in an FM contract vary but will include facility operations, maintenance and asset management.

Financial Close: Successful culmination of the activities leading up to the signature of a PFI contract. It requires the official approval from the relevant authority that allows the awarding authority to sign the contract, the approval of the funders for the SPV to sign the contract and the fulfilment by the SPV of all the pre-conditions set out in the agreed draft contracts.

Financial Model: Bidders for a PFI project are required to submit a financial model of their costings and charges, showing how these depend upon the values of certain variables. Inter alia, this enables sensitivity testing, to explore how cash flows, or other financial outcomes, would be affected by hypothetical changes in assumed values for these variables.

Financing Cost: Costs arising from the financing of the capital costs of the PFI contract.

Functional Specifications: Those specifications that define the function or duty to be performed by the product. E.g. document filing and retrieving system. (See HM Treasury [1991], p.2).

Governance Structures: A transaction occurs whenever "a good or service is transferred across a technologically separable interface". All such transactions require a structure of governance, to resolve potential disputes between transactors. Two generic types of governance structure are: *unified* governance, also known as 'hierarchy', where both transactors are brought under a common ownership and a single internal authority for dispute resolution; and *market* governance, where general law of contract, enforced by the courts, is used for dispute resolution. In addition, specialised types of transaction may justify the establishment of transaction-specific (or bilateral) governance structures.

Hard FM: Provision of sites and buildings, fit-outs and adaptations, operations and maintenance of buildings.

Incomplete Contracts: See Section 2.5, p.17.

Incremental Innovation: Defined in Section 2.3, p.11

Input: Resources used to achieve a goal.

Mathematical Risk: Simple variation or degree of dispersion of a set of outcomes around the mean or average outcome for all of that set. See Section 2.2, p.8.

Mean: Representative average value.

Median: Value that splits a distribution in half. I.e. 50% of the observed values are higher or equal to the median and 50% of the observed values are lower or equal to the median.

Mode: Observed value with the highest frequency.

One-Off Project: A project which is 'free standing' in the eyes of all key project participants, and is not evaluated as part of a larger programme of projects or continuing commercial relationship between participants.

Operational Cost Saving: Costs can be divided into initial or capital costs (q.v.) and subsequent or operational costs. Operational costs in any year will normally be covered by operating revenues of the same year, but may nevertheless generate a requirement for working capital finance. An operational cost saving thus represents an increase in the net annual surplus of revenues over operating costs in each year of operation of the facility. Additionally, it may, but need not, represent a reduction in the requirement for working capital finance. See also 'Capital Cost Saving'

Operator: The firm responsible for providing the service that is the fulfilment of any PFI contract, to whose delivery payments throughout the duration of that contract are tied. This is sometimes the PFI company itself, but sometimes a firm with a contract to supply operating services to the PFI company.

Opportunism: See Section 2.5, p.17.

Output: Objectives, production, yield, result.

Output Specifications: Statement of the needs to be satisfied in terms of objectives, production or result rather than in terms of the inputs necessary to achieve those objectives.

Out-turn Cost: The ex-post or actual cost incurred by a project client; its excess over the ex-ante cost estimate or tender price is referred to as the cost overrun.

Perception of Risk: See Section 2.2, p.8.

Performance Specifications: Those specifications that define the performance required from an item, e.g. device capable of moving 50 tonnes of grain an hour from a silo to a bagging plant 50 metres away (See HM Treasury [1991], p.2).

PFI Client: See Awarding Authority.

PFI Company: See Special Purpose Vehicle (SPV)

Preliminary Design: Designs carried out previously to the tender of the PFI contract, which constitute part of the reference documentation for the bidders.

Prescriptive Specifications: Those specifications which prescribe the solution to be adopted, rather than describe the problem to be solved; and which thereby restrict the choices of solution open to the provider. Normally, it is assumed that technical specifications are likely to be prescriptive.

Principal Designer: Firm that carries out the main design effort (at least at the strategic level) on behalf of the SPV of the PFI contract.

Product Enhancing Innovation: Innovation that implies value-increasing solutions by providing an improved product or service for which the customer is prepared to pay more. See Section 2.3, p.11.

Public Sector Client: See Awarding Authority.

Quartile: A range between a pair of values that contains one fourth of the total population when equally divided.

Radical Innovation: Defined in Section 2.3, p.11

Risk: In the context of this text, a situation in which it is possible quantitatively to assess the probability of a future outcome for a given situation, based on current data and information.

Risk Averse: See Section 2.2, p.8.

Risk Neutral: See Section 2.2, p.8.

Risk Transfer: See 'Value of Risk Transfer' in Section 2.2, p.8.

Signed Contracts / Deals: PFI projects that have passed financial close, and where therefore, a PFI contract has been awarded and activated.

Soft FM: Allocation of space, services and equipment to meet management objectives and user needs through time.

Special Purpose Vehicle (SPV): Legal entity that is created by shareholders in a bidding company or consortium if it is successful. This entity contracts with the public sector client for the purpose of delivering the PFI service. It is normally legally formed just prior to financial close.

Specifications: Statement of the needs to be satisfied by the procurement of external resources (definition taken from HM Treasury [1991])

SPV's Supplier: Organisation supplying some sort of service to the SPV.

Technical Specifications: Those specifications that define the technical and physical characteristics of an item in terms of such things as physical dimensions, materials used, number of doors and windows, their location and dimension and so on. (See HM Treasury [1991], p.2).

Third Party Revenue: Opportunity of revenue for the SPV or PFI company, which results from the utilisation of the PFI project assets for purposes different from those that constitute the reason for the contract. E.g. opportunity of hiring out sport facilities of a PFI school to a third party, outside the time in which the school makes use of those facilities.

Transaction Cost Economics: As used in Section 2.4, p.15.

Uncertainty: It exists in situations where there is insufficient data to be able to make a probabilistic estimate of a future outcome.

Value of Risk Transfer: See Section 2.2, p. 8.

Whole-life Costing: Whole-life costs are simply the sum (discounted to a common year's equivalent values) of capital and operating costs (q.q.v.) over the whole expected economic life of a facility. A whole-life costing approach to investment decision-making takes discounted operational costs into account, as well as capital costs.

Note: For more definitions and exemplification of most of the specialised terms used in PFI projects, see CIC [1998].

Executive summary

The aim of this study is to identify the role that Cost Savings and Innovations have played in PFI construction-based projects so far. To achieve this, a wide survey among PFI project managers was carried out. Additionally, and in order to illustrate the results arising from the survey, case studies were carried out. The main text presents a theoretical framework for the report, a detailed account of the measurements and opinions collected, an analysis of the explanatory factors for the extent of cost savings, a set of three sectoral studies, and two case studies.

Key findings

Cost savings reported, all projects

(a) The median reported design, build and operate (DBO) cost saving is between 5% and 10% (Chapter 3, Section 3.4).

(b) The range of reported DBO cost savings is from a maximum of over 20% savings (identified on three projects in our survey) to a minimum of between 10% to 20% increase (on two projects in our survey) (Appendices A.6 and A.8).

(c) Just over one-third of respondents reported DBO cost savings of 10% or more (Appendices A.6 and A.8).

Cost savings reported, by type of project

In the following table, two sets of results are presented. First, the general reported cost savings found in the survey, ordered by type of facility. Second, an analysis of such results classified by five different explanatory variables (of which, four constituted hypotheses of the research).

	Descriptor	Median total DBO cost saving:	Median construction cost saving:	Percentage reporting total DBO saving of 5% or over
Results by type of facility	Education	5% saving to 5% increase	5% saving to 5% increase	22%
	Healthcare	5% saving to 5% increase	5% saving to 5% increase	35%
	Accommodation	Savings of 5-10%	5% saving to 5% increase	58%
	Custodial	Savings of 10-20%	Savings of 10-20%	88%
	Transport	Savings of 10-20%	Savings over 20%	84%
Results by explanatory factors	With centralised clients	Savings of 10-20%	Savings of 5-10%	83%
	With decentralised clients (Section 4.2 and A.8)	5% saving to 5% increase	5% saving to 5% increase	31%
	Complete service	Savings of 10-20%	Savings of 10-20%	81%
	Partial service (Section 4.5 and A.8)	5% saving to 5% increase	5% saving to 5% increase	38%
	Largest 50% of projects	Savings of 5-10%	Savings of 5-10%	65%
	Smallest 50% of projects (Section 4.4 and A.8)	Savings of 5-10%	5% saving to 5% increase	52%
	With technical content to OS	Savings of 5-10%	5% saving to 5% increase	78%
	Without technical content to OS (Section 4.6 and A.8)	Savings of 5-10%	Savings of 5-10%	61%
	Building-based	5% saving to 5% increase	5% saving to 5% increase	49%
	Civil engineering-based (Section 4.3 and A.8)	Savings of 10-20%	Savings of 10-20%	84%

It can be seen that two out of four factors originally proposed as explanatory of the variation in cost saving were as hypothesised ('centralised clients' and 'complete service'). However, two of them do not work as expected ('size of project' and 'form of output specification'). Moreover, an unexpected factor ('civil engineering-based projects') arose from the analysis of the survey's results.

Cost savings reported, by type of cost (Chapter 3, Section 3.4)

Over all projects, the percentage median cost savings reported were:

Total costs:	savings of 5-10%	Core operating costs:	savings of 5-10%
Construction costs:	savings of 5-10%	Preliminary costs:	5% savings to 5% increase
FM costs:	savings of 5-10%	Other fees:	Increases of 10-20%

The 'weights' of these components of cost are unequal on average, and vary substantially from project to project. Overall, construction costs seem to have the highest average weight, i.e. account for the highest single proportion of total DBU costs.

Inefficiencies in traditional procurement and provision (Chapter 3, Sections 3.2 and 3.3)

Pre-PFI procurement and provision was regarded as relatively efficient by respondents in transport, healthcare, accommodation and housing projects, and as least efficient by respondents in custodial projects. This seems to explain, in large part, why custodial PFI projects report among the highest cost-saving innovations (CSIs) and cost savings, but it makes the outcome for transport projects more surprising.

Sources and circumstances of innovation (Chapter 3, Section 3.5)

Innovations in civil engineering projects are reported to be mainly technological, whereas innovations in building projects are much less frequently technologically based.

This may explain, in large part, why civil engineering PFI projects report among the highest levels of CSIs and cost savings. It suggests that incentive to innovate is not enough. It helps greatly if there are also identified focus opportunities for innovation, such as those to introduce new pavement materials in highways.

Opinions regarding appropriateness of PFI processes

The main area of the process in respect to which respondents expressed dissatisfaction was output specifications (OS).

(a) Only one-quarter of SPV respondents rated the clients' OS as 'highly appropriate'. In many cases these respondents thought that the OS used were still at least in part 'technical' or prescriptive (Chapter 3, Section 3.6).

Despite this strong private sector opinion that such OS are less appropriate, we found no clear relationship between the form of OS and the extent of cost saving (Sections 4.6 and A.8).

(b) Public sector responses were divided in their levels of satisfaction with the process and product of writing OS. Centralised clients were mainly satisfied with what they were able to achieve, and regarded the main unsolved problem as the inherently intractable one of imperfect foresight over very long contract periods. Decentralised clients thought that they lacked experience, capacity and time to write good OS (Section 3.6).

Recommendations to the public sector to improve VFM from PFI

(a) Take steps to maximise the benefits of PFI experience gathered to date within the public sector, and to reduce the number of PFI projects procured by unsupported, inexperienced public sector managers.

(b) Allow more time at the invitation to negotiate (ITN) stage of bids, in some instances for the development of innovative proposals, or alternatively give a positive weighting to innovative proposals in bid evaluation.

(c) Identify and target some promising areas in terms of potential for innovation, and then prioritise these in terms of bringing projects to the market.

(d) Concentrate the scarce resource of public sector PFI expertise on types of project where best value review reveals the established public sector procurement and provision to be relatively less efficient.

(e) Commission an investigation to assess what actions or changes, if any, would significantly improve potential cost savings for types of client and project for which results to date have been least impressive.

(f) Decentralised clients, such as local authorities and NHS Trusts, should create arrangements providing for the transfer or secondment within the public sector of staff with the appropriate skills and experience.

(g) Create a group of professional public sector managers, possibly directly employed by the Office of Government Commerce, who, as part of their career, work on a series of projects.

(h) Consider the setting up of specialised PFI Procurement Agencies to act on behalf of decentralised clients so that PFI projects could be more effectively procured, in terms of value for money (VFM).

(i) Commission further research to identify 'key' attributes of highly effective (and, indeed, of highly ineffective) OS.

(j) Publish further guidance suggesting how PFI procurement can be improved in terms of asset and service OS.

Chapter 1 # Introduction

Synopsis

Amongst other goals, the Private Finance Initiative (PFI) has been seen as a way of achieving, for the public sector, the Egan Report objective of better client *value for money* (VFM) from construction-based projects, by 'rethinking' the construction process. Studies of PFI to date have shown substantial variation, from project to project, in the VFM improvement achieved. This study tested the Egan proposition by asking the people responsible for managing PFI projects for their opinions about the extent of improved VFM cost saving achieved in their projects, in the costs of construction and operation of facilities. The study also sought to discover the main reasons for the reported variation in project achievement of cost savings. To do this we focused on factors affecting the extent of *innovation* achieved in a PFI project. We call these factors *enablers* and *inhibitors* of innovation.

Note that the cost savings discussed throughout this report refer to the costs of designing, building and operating (DBO), but not to the costs of financing projects. Costs of finance involve completely separate issues, unrelated to innovating and achieving efficiencies in the design, construction and operation of built facilities.

Note also that throughout this report the data discussed represent the *opinions* of informed and expert respondents, from all parts of the PFI industry, including both private and public sectors; but this data is explicitly *subjective* and not based on attempts at an 'objective' accounting of cost savings or of innovations.

1.1 Scope and limitations

The review carried out by the Construction Taskforce, led by Sir John Egan (entitled *'Rethinking construction'*, Egan, 1998), raised a series of proposals to improve quality and efficiency in UK construction. Despite accepting that the UK construction industry at its best was excellent, the report also acknowledged that the industry as a whole was underachieving. It argued that the industry had low profitability, invested too little in capital, R&D and training, and that too many of the industry's clients were dissatisfied with its overall performance. At the same time, the radical change and improvements that other industries have demonstrated were said to be perfectly applicable throughout the construction industry, making them available to all its clients.

For that reason, the Egan Report proposed ambitious targets and supported an effective measurement of performance. According to the experience of the Taskforce members, these targets are necessary and achievable. However, targets are not enough if they are not set together with performance appraisal. The proposed objectives therefore take the form of an annual percentile saving for each of the following: capital cost, construction time, predictability, defects, accidents, productivity, turnover and profits. In particular, it is proposed to achieve a cumulative 10% *per annum* capital cost saving and an annual 20% decrease in the number of defects – in order to achieve a zero-defect standard in a period of five years.

To achieve these targets, *Rethinking Construction* argues that radical changes are necessary, first, in the process through which the industry delivers its projects, and second, in the culture and structure of the industry. The former should be carried through by the creation of an integrated project process around four key elements: product development; project implementation; partnering the supply chain; and production of components. The latter should be achieved through the provision of decent and safe working conditions and improvement of management and supervisory skills at all levels. Sustained improvement is to be delivered through the use of techniques for eliminating waste and increasing value for the customer, while projects should be designed for ease of construction, making maximum use of standard components and processes.

In the same report (p.39), it is indicated that

"the Government has already demonstrated through Public–Private Partnerships and the PFI its ability to make radical and successful changes in its procurement policies."

These would have carried the possibility of tapping

"a rich seam of ingenuity which previously had been stifled by the traditional processes of prescriptive design and tendering."

It is therefore timely to ask a series of questions:

- To what extent has the public sector, through its PFI clients, made a radical change in its way of procuring when using PFI?
- Has that change been successful?
- Is it true that PFI has tapped a rich seam of ingenuity that previously was stifled by prescriptive design and tendering?
- Is PFI actually helping to achieve the goals proposed by the Egan Report?
- Are the savings achieved through the use of PFI, if any, being rightly appraised?
- Has PFI created a well-integrated process from which the generation of radical changes is possible?
- Is PFI producing a cultural change through the provision of more decent working conditions and the improvement of management and supervisory skills at all levels?
- Did 'prescriptive designs and procurement' really stifle the achievement of value for money? And is PFI eliminating that hindrance?
- Are there any characteristics of some PFI projects that enable them to tap greater ingenuity, or to achieve greater value for money than others?

The argument in favour of PFI is based on presumed greater economic efficiency of private sector supply, or *provision*, of services required and *purchased* by the public sector. PFI contracts are also known as DBFO, standing for Design, Build, Finance and

Operate. These four functions related to built assets underlie the final provision of services obtained by operating those assets. Considering these four functions, PFI, in comparison to conventional public sector provision, clearly raises the costs associated with financing. In fact, what PFI has to do to achieve value for money is to counteract the increased cost of borrowing, advisers' fees and private sector profit through innovation and appropriate risk transfer, in order to save cost per unit of value in the functions of design, construction and operation. This can be done by reducing the cost of providing similar services, providing an improved service at the same cost, or a combination of both. The reduction of cost per unit of value would have to come, under the stimulus of the transfer of risk and reward to the private sector, from either private sector efficiencies in production, requiring less input per unit of output, or the purchase or procurement of cheaper inputs. Therefore, one key question is whether or not the extra costs associated with private finance in PFI have been offset by the improvements in performance of production (design, construction and operation of built assets).

In this respect, the existing evidence is inconclusive. Publications exist which indicate that PFI fails to achieve this balance. For example, Unison (1999) p.34, in a study of the North Durham Acute Hospitals PFI scheme, suggests that the project fails to demonstrate extra efficiency and even demands reductions in budgets of clinical services.

"In order to meet the PFI bill, staffing budgets are being cut back, meaning that the remaining clinical staff will have to work to heroic productivity targets just to maintain current levels of provision, while inpatient admissions will have to be reduced below the anticipated level of demand."

On the other hand, other reports suggest the opposite. For instance, the National Audit Office (NAO) report on PRIME, the Department of Social Security's (DSS) deal on the transference and running of their offices, shows a clear success for PFI. The NAO (1999) considered that the deal was well planned, the bidding and contracting process was successfully handled, the department chose the best deal and that the deal represents better value for money than using public borrowing and conventional procurement.

However, the same NAO, in an interview (Financial Times, 15 Dec.1999) given by Mr Jeremy Colman – Head of PFI audit at the NAO – accepts that that there is an *"extraordinary variation between different deals. It absolutely depends on the circumstances. Do they favour PFI or not? And how skilfully has the deal been struck? Some people are very good at managing deals, others are still learning."*

In the above interview, the Prison Service and the Highways Agency are highlighted as being able to commission value-for-money PFI deals, despite some initial question marks. The explanation offered is that, unlike other Public Agencies, they have not wasted their pool of PFI talent and experience. That is, they have reused staff with PFI experience on subsequent PFI projects.

"People who have done deals know far more than they can easily communicate about how to do deals. And therefore, the best way would be to get them to do more."

Up to December 1999 the NAO had undertaken reviews of eleven PFI projects or groups of projects. In seven of these, the public sector was able to undertake comparison of the net present cost (NPC) of the PFI contract with the net present cost of the public sector comparator (the cost of a publicly funded alternative means of attaining the same objectives by producing similar service outputs – PSC). These seven reports included five built-asset based groups comprising nine projects: highways (two groups or studies comprising five projects); prisons (one study of two projects); a hospital; and PRIME (the DSS office estate).

As well as construction and operating costs, this method of comparison includes financing costs (following Treasury guidelines by using a public sector financing real discount rate of 6%, plus allowance for inflation), and an explicit valuation of risk transferred from the public sector by having a 'guaranteed' PFI contract, especially in terms of construction cost and time guarantees.

The NAO's estimates of value for money (saving in NPC) on these five groups range from 3% (Dartford & Gravesham Hospital) through 8–12% (roads and prisons) to 22% (PRIME), with a value-weighted mean of 17%.

However, not only does PRIME dominate the weighting as by far the largest project (if it and NIRS 2 are removed from the sample, the mean savings become 10%), but also the other projects in the NAO set are heavily weighted towards roads and prisons which, as we shall see, is likely to have had an appreciable effect on the size of the NAO average cost-saving figure.

A somewhat more broadly based study has been undertaken for the Treasury Taskforce by management consultants Arthur Andersen and the London School of Economics and Political Science (LSE). This compared NPCs for PFI and public sector comparators (PSCs) on 29 projects and, as with the NAO studies, included both cost of finance and value of risk transfer. It found an average cost saving of 17%, 10 percentage points of which arose from the valuation of risk transfer. Andersen and LSE were unable to take into account PFI proposals rejected on VFM grounds, or to develop an alternative methodology of estimating VFM in cases without a PSC.

These savings found in the project NPCs show a wide range and high dispersion about the mean. In 7 cases out of 29, the saving is shown as 5% or less, but in 11 cases as 20% or more. Of the 29 projects, 14 show cost savings of 12% or less (calculated from data provided in Andersen/LSE Report, section 5.4). Thus, the median value of cost saving in the Andersen/LSE study is just over 12%.

The Andersen/LSE Report contains some interesting findings on factors that appear to explain some of this variance.

- Some public sector organisations have experienced much lower rates of construction cost and time overruns on their projects than have others (ranging from average cost overruns of 3% to an average of 18%). Thus, the valuation to be placed on risk transfer (see Chapter 2) itself varies between types of public sector client, and this accounts for a significant part of the variation in estimated cost savings.
- Estimated NPC savings are positively correlated with the share of capital expenditure in total project expenditure. Andersen/LSE's interpretation of this finding is that, proportionately, PFI cost savings have been greater in design and construction (and whole-life 'hard' facility management costs associated with these) and lower in other aspects of operating costs.

The Andersen/LSE Report also contains a survey of PFI public sector project managers that has similarities in approach to the present study. It contains analysis of the responses from 22 such project managers, responsible for 34 projects. The authors posited 18 'drivers' of VFM in a PFI project.

Of these 18 drivers, the respondents found the following 6 to be most important in affecting VFM:

- risks transferred being priced by the private sector at less than the value of risk transfer to the public sector
- having output-based (i.e. not input-based or 'prescriptive') specifications
- having the scope for whole-life costing approach to design and construction given by long-term contracts
- having performance indicators and measures linked to payment mechanisms
- having effective price-led competition between rival bidders
- having opportunity to apply private sector management skills to achieve operational efficiencies.

Proposed drivers reported to be relatively unimportant included:

- extra scope created by the bundling of smaller projects
- scope to achieve third party revenues
- scope for release of hidden asset value in assets previously held by public sector.

The present study commenced before the Andersen/LSE study, and its survey was completed before results from the Andersen/LSE study became available. The drivers we have explored overlap with, but are by no means the same as, the drivers examined by Andersen/LSE.

This report allows a comparison of our findings with those of the Andersen/LSE Report. However, it should be made clear that the estimated median cost savings in this report, of 5% to 10%, are not directly comparable with the 17% mean, and 12% median found in the Andersen study; nor indeed has a directly comparable methodology been followed by our respondents.

Because we were surveying private as well as public sector respondents, and because risk transfer valuation is not always costed separately in the full business case (FBC), not all of our respondents were in a position to follow the approved public sector methodology, for separate measurement of the value of risk transfer. Our private sector respondents were left free to choose their own benchmarks, and to draw on their own experience to make project cost comparisons (see Chapter 3 and Appendix A.1 Methodology). Our public sector respondents, however, will have included a risk transfer element in their overall comparison.

Moreover, our survey is not confined to projects for which a directly comparable PSC existed. This may account for some of the differences between our findings and those in the Andersen/LSE Report (see Chapter 3, Section 3.10).

At least one adjustment would be needed to make like-for-like comparison possible. Full data does not exist to permit this adjustment to be made with real accuracy. Financing costs are included in the Andersen/LSE study but not in this study. Moreover, it is possible that differences in the treatment of some categories of procurement process costs exist.

However, the main aim of the present study is not to contribute to the search for an accurate accounting measure of the mean or median cost saving achieved in PFI, but to explore why VFM in PFI projects shows such substantial variation, and to examine the implications of that explanation. Hence, any comparison between the figures in this study and those published by the NAO and in the Andersen/LSE Report needs to be treated with caution.

The objective of this piece of work is to contribute to the understanding of whether and how cost saving and innovation have been fostered and subsequently implemented in PFI. It has sought to identify variables that affect the presence of those cost savings and innovation, relating both to the public and the private sector. In particular, this report focuses on construction and operating cost outcomes and the cost-saving innovations (CSIs) giving rise to them. The report proceeds by investigating both the direct and tangible type of innovation, such as cost-saving design, construction techniques or operating regimes, and innovation in the organisation of the process of provision – such as in the type of organisational arrangements, the methods of specification and the methods used for managing the PFI concession.

In the course of the research for the CIC's *Constructors' key guide to PFI* (CIC, 1998), it became clear that the ability of the PFI bidders to provide innovative solutions to many of the PFI projects had not been as widespread as expected by some early proponents of PFI. The obstacles to innovation identified by participants were attributed to both sides. Some public sector clients were said to have written highly detailed and comprehensive documents forming the output specifications (OS), which had inhibited innovation, or were said to have been unwilling to accept significant innovation, which they perceived as creating too great a risk. On the bidders' side, there was said to have been a reluctance or inability to propose any radically innovative schemes.

Therefore, this research focused on a wide range of postulated *enablers* and *inhibitors* of innovation, on the extent to which these were found to be present in the projects comprising the set of 'signed' construction-related PFIs, and the extent to which they were associated with the amount of cost saving and innovation achieved.

The research does not attempt to provide detailed worked examples indicating exact cost savings, nor to give detailed descriptions (or even lists) of specific innovations identified. Our discussions with participants had indicated clearly to us the problem that commercial confidentiality would pose in a highly competitive environment to any such attempts. Moreover, 'technical' descriptions of particular innovations would necessarily be highly case-specific, and reveal little about the *process* of search for innovation and cost saving in PFI as a whole. Finally, the audited and structured quantified data required for systematic measurement of out-turn PFI costs, and their comparison with costs of alternative modes of procurement and provision, is lacking.

At the time of the research, a large proportion of 'signed deals' had not progressed to the point at which out-turn construction costs could be measured, and very few possessed data on even one year's observed actual operating costs. Moreover, meaningful cost data must be comparative and, by definition, actual out-turn cost data cannot exist for the 'counter-factual', the public sector alternative not actually chosen. This leaves only *ex ante* estimates and predictions of cost as a potential source for measurement and comparison, and it is these that have been used.

Such estimates are the basis, project by project, for the value-for-money comparison of the PFI option, including the value for money comparator (VFMC), required by HM Treasury before approval is given to proceed with a PFI project. For the

PFI term in the comparison, the figures used, although only estimates of cost, are elements in the financial model used to arrive at the *fixed* contract *price*. If the estimates transpire, in the out-turn, to differ from actual costs, it is the private sector PFI company or consortium that will bear the loss or take the extra profit. Thus, if strong competitive pressure exists throughout the bidding and negotiation process, it is reasonable to take these prices as a proxy for the PFI company's 'best estimate' of probable costs. Unfortunately, the highly variable basis on which the VFMC are calculated makes the second term in the comparison less robust and useful for research. The implications of this for the research are discussed in Chapter 2. It is sufficient to note here that rather than seek to find agreement on an 'objective' measure of construction and operating cost comparisons, we chose to ask each participant in a project for their informed but 'subjective' opinion of the cost difference, allowing these to vary for different respondents on the same project.

To the extent to which the research has succeeded in identifying the more significant *enablers* and *inhibitors*, we believe that it constitutes a valuable contribution to the knowledge-base for public sector policy and decision making in the private and public sectors, and to the clarification of central issues for the provision of public services and PFI / PPP procurement in the UK.

1.2 Structure of the report

This report is structured to follow closely the different stages of the methodology of work. The theoretical framework of the research is discussed in Chapter 2. Some readers might find it more appropriate to skip this chapter and to go straight to the results presented thereafter. The purpose of this chapter is to explain *why* we identified certain factors as potentially important enablers and inhibitors of innovation.

Chapter 3 details the main findings from the extensive survey of signed construction-related PFI projects. The analysis is carried out in different ways, according to the particular issues being examined. Details of the statistical operations and tests performed and the exhaustive description of the responses are included in the Appendices. Most of the results refer to the whole sample or comparisons between all its constituent subgroups.

Chapters 4 and 5 explore the differences in approach that are discernible by 'drilling' into the data that the survey has generated. In this part of the report the principal hypotheses of the research are tested. In Chapter 4, the influence of the main supporters and inhibitors of cost saving are shown and discussed. This discussion, for example, contrasts infrastructure projects with building projects; centralised clients with dispersed clients; and full service provision with secondary service provision. Chapter 5 goes on illustrating these differences with a benchmarking exercise among three principal sectors of PFI projects: the custodial sector, the healthcare sector and the highways sector.

Chapter 6 explores two case studies. Selected to exemplify a number of facets of PFI generally found within the present population of PFI projects, they aim to embody and illustrate the previously developed discussion.

Finally, Chapter 7 draws out the principal conclusions and makes recommendations to policy makers, clients and the supply side for fostering an environment conducive to innovation.

Chapter 2 — Explanation of the theoretical framework used in this research

Synopsis

This chapter defines some of the more complex key concepts used in, or underpinning, the study. The simpler concepts are defined briefly in the Glossary. It also contains an explanation of *why* we chose to advance and test certain propositions regarding factors likely to act as *inhibitors* or *enablers* of cost-saving innovation.

This chapter, and Appendix A.1 Methodology, will be of most interest to academic readers. Other readers may wish to pass directly to Chapter 3, returning to Chapter 2 only if they find it necessary in order to understand more about the background to the explanatory variables used in the main body of the report.

2.1 Efficiency gains

Over the whole PFI programme, the reduction in cost/improvement in value sought would have to come either from improvements in average 'unit productivity' (ratios of value of outputs of services produced to the units or quantities of inputs used), or from reductions in the prices paid for inputs of similar unit productivity.

The stimulus for both kinds of improvement in the value/cost ratio (VFM) is presumed to come from the *strong profit incentives* created for the private sector by PFI contracts by means of the transfer of risk and reward to the private sector provider, and from the *improved opportunity to innovate* created for the private sector by integrated design/ build/finance/operate (DBFO) contracts, compared to separate or fragmented contracts.

2.2 Value of risk transfer

All the above section refers to averages and actual outcomes. There is also presumed to be valuable benefit to the public sector if, by PFI, it can produce a reduction in *variation* (increased predictability) of individual project outcomes around their average outcome, and obtain *earlier certainty* of what those out-turn project costs and values will be.

This benefit is referred to in the PFI literature as the value of risk transfer. The measurement of the value that should be attached to such reductions in variation and earlier certainty has been controversial, in the context of PFI. Resolution of this controversy has not been assisted by the conceptual confusion between:

- mathematical risk *and* perceptual risk
- risk reduction for a project *and* for a portfolio of projects.

In brief, mathematical risk refers to simple variation or degree of dispersion of a set of outcomes around the mean or average outcome for all of that set. This is illustrated in Fig. 2.1.

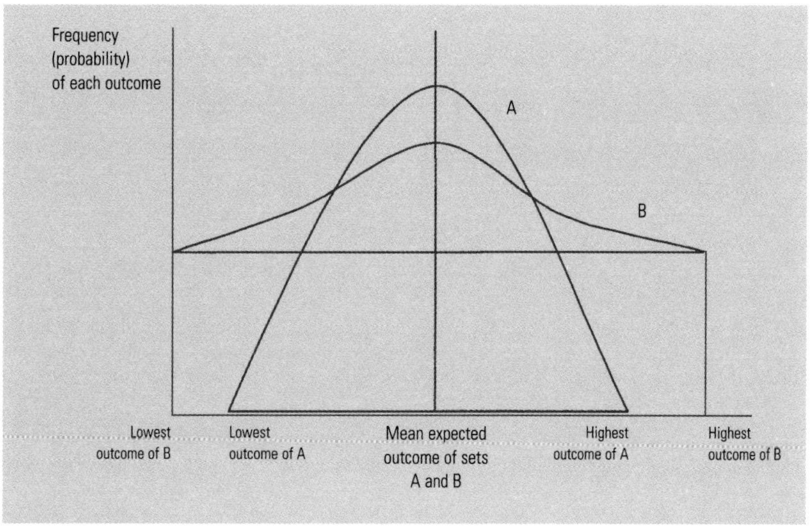

Figure 2.1 *Mathematical risk*

Risk in this case is the probability of obtaining an outcome, in any one case, that is significantly different from the mean outcome that will result from a whole set or portfolio of projects. 'Difference' here means, equally, outcomes 'better than' as well as 'worse than' the average. An economic decision maker is said to be *risk averse* if they prefer (would choose) the range of possible outcomes shown by distribution A to that shown by distribution B, and would be prepared to pay some amount to replace B by A; and is said to be *risk neutral* if they have no preference between A and B.

The larger the set or portfolio of projects belonging to the decision maker, the more likely it is that the *actual* average outcome of their portfolio will approach the *expected* average, predicted on the basis of knowledge of the relevant mathematical probabilities. Thus, one reason for risk aversion is removed.

From this perspective, therefore, the public sector considered as a single entity has less cause to be willing to pay to replace B with A than any other purchaser of projects, since it has the largest portfolio.

However, the following points can be made against this conclusion. Fig. 2.1 does not accurately represent how project risks are *perceived* by public sector clients and their advisers. Portfolio risk theory assumes that outcomes for any one project in the set are determined independently of outcomes for any other project. It also assumes that the forecast or expectation supplied by experts to the decision maker measures a true mean (average) of known probabilities. Whereas here, neither are projects sufficiently similar to permit future probabilities for Set A or Set B to be calculated from data on past projects, or from a mathematical simulation; nor do the expert forecasts supplied for a single project represent the mean outcome to be expected if that 'same' project were to be procured many times over. Rather, the forecast is, at best, an estimate of the modal (most likely single) outcome. And, to make matters worse, the nature of the distribution of possible outcomes is such that the mode lies towards one extreme end of the range of probable outcomes, as shown in Fig. 2.2.

The largest single proportion of projects procured are within a few percentage

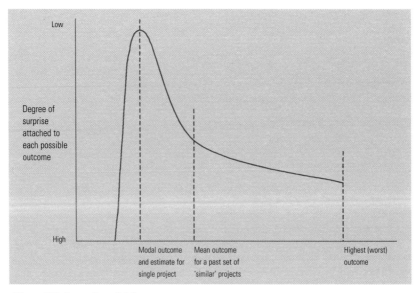

Figure 2.2 *Perception of risk*

points of being 'on budget' and 'on time', i.e. their outcome is roughly that predicted by the expert estimator. However, while a significant proportion of projects have outcomes that are much worse than this, only a negligible number of projects (if any) have outcomes that are significantly better.

However, the decision maker should not shoot the estimator, who may have done the best professional job possible given the circumstances and brief. If the expert is asked to produce a single-figure estimate of 'likely' out-turn cost (or time, or value) they can hardly do anything better than accurately estimate the mode (most likely single value). This maximises the likelihood that their estimate will be within a few percentage points of the actual outcome.

Moreover, note that in Fig. 2.2 the vertical axis does not show (precise, known) probabilities but (imprecise, imagined) *degrees of potential surprise* (Hillebrandt, 1985). This reflects the fact that the estimator's problem is not to predict the results from repeatedly rolling a pair of (identical, unloaded) dice, but to predict the outcome for a project that is, to a largely unknown degree, different from or similar to other projects for which out-turn costs are known. Thus, while the difference between the average estimate and average out-turn for that set of past projects can, in principle, be known ('average cost overrun on projects procured by this department in the last five years was $y\%$'), the estimator has no secure basis in knowledge on which to extrapolate from that observed difference to a single revised estimate for the present single project. Nevertheless, we can understand that the decision maker will have come to regard the single-figure estimates supplied by their expert advisers as, in an aggregate sense, 'underestimates'.

The nature of the contracts conventionally used by the public sector, prior to PFI, has been such that a significant part of the risk associated with 'underestimation' has been borne by the public sector. That is, although competitive tendering has been used to establish what at first sight look like fixed, lump-sum tender prices, the contract terms and conditions have been such that the risks of out-turn costs being above the contractors' estimate (tender price) have at best been shared between public sector client and contractor. The same has been true of time out-turn risk.

The situation with respect to divergence between estimated and out-turn costs of operating public sector facilities has been broadly analogous to that described above for construction costs. That is, there are sound reasons for thinking that operating cost estimates will also (if the promised quantity of service standard is enforced), in out-turn, tend on average to be underestimated.

Now, when contracts are signed on a PFI project (which is, admittedly, not at a very early stage in the life of the project as an investment proposal), the client is supplied, not with an estimate, but with a promise, backed up by an enforceable contract, with good penalties for non-performance on time or value (quality) and a guaranteed price. Therefore, it is equally understandable that such a client may consider it money well spent to enter into such a contract, even if at a somewhat higher price than the sum of the estimates of construction cost and operating cost (and time, and value) for a traditional (non-PFI) procurement of the same project and service. The value attached by the client to that difference between 'guarantee' and 'estimate' is the meaning of the 'value of risk transfer' in appraisal of PFI prices against the public sector comparator (PSC), insofar as it refers to mundane project risks, and not to exceptional ones (acts of God, *force majeure*, legislation, etc.).

2.3 Thinking about innovation as an activity whose product is cost saving

According to Rogers [1983], *invention* is the process or activity by which a new idea is discovered or created. Freeman [1989] presents a similar definition, considering that an *invention* is a detailed design or model of a process or product that can clearly be distinguished as novel compared to existing arts.

On the other hand, *innovation* can be defined as the process or activity of seeking, recognising and implementing a new technology or process to improve the functions which an organisation is performing. Freeman considers an *innovation* to be the actual use of non-trivial change and improvement in a process, product, or system that is novel to the institution developing the change. In particular, a *construction innovation* would be produced when a construction firm makes the first use of an existing technology or process, for a particular function or purpose, within its organisation. For the purposes of this project, an *innovation* is understood to be an action performed by any participant in the PFI process that introduces a novel way of carrying out a function or achieving a goal.

The way in which the process of *construction innovation* is generated is the subject of discussion in the literature. In fact, several models and descriptions have been developed. For the purposes of this research, a simple model has been assumed, which is shown in Fig. 2.3 (source: Laborde and Sanvido, 1994).

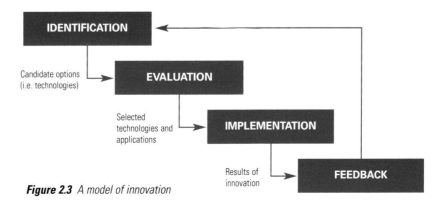

Figure 2.3 A model of innovation

Types of innovation

In terms of the types of innovation that this report considers, two principal classifications are used. The first classifies the types of innovation according to the scope of their effects over the relevant process; and the second, according to the way in which they produce those effects on the outcome of the PFI project.

The first classification comes from the mainstream theories of innovation in manufacturing, which in turn are based on current theories in management and economics. This classification considers five different types of innovation: incremental innovations; modular innovations; architectural innovations; system innovations; and radical innovations (Slaughter, 1998). These are illustrated in Fig. 2.4.

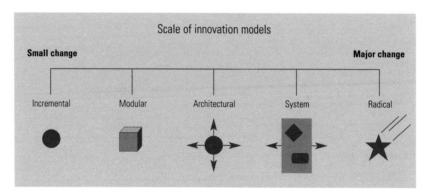

Figure 2.4 *Five models of innovation (source: Slaughter, 1998)*

The issues at the moment of implementing these innovations will be essentially of timing (of the commitment to use the innovation), coordination (among the members of the project), special resources required (for its implementation) and the nature of the supervisory activities required.

- An *incremental innovation* implies a small change based upon current technology and experience. Its source is typically within the same organisation that is implementing it.

- A *modular innovation* involves a significant change in concept within a component, but leaves the links to other components and systems unchanged. In construction, their source could be from organisations that have existing control over and responsibility for the module, or from a new entrant.

- An *architectural innovation* involves a small change within a component, but a major change in the links to the other components and systems. That is, it changes the 'architecture' that links elements and organisations within a structured process. Its developers are most often an organisation that does not have a vested interest in maintaining the existing linkages but at the same time understands the required linkage changes.

- A *system innovation* is typically identified through its integration of multiple independent innovations that must work together to perform new functions or improve the facility performance as a whole. Their sources are found in those who are not interested in maintaining the existing configuration.

- Finally, a *radical innovation* implies the existence of a breakthrough in science or technology that often changes the character of the industry. Its source is often from outside an existing industry and is based on scientific or engineering research.

A second classification of the types of innovation is necessary when thinking about innovation in the PFI project. This considers two broad types of innovation: cost-saving innovation and product enhancing innovation. These are defined as the two ways by which the efficiency of providing a product or service may be improved. The former implies a reduction in costs, through cost-saving innovative solutions, while leaving the value of the product or service unchanged. The latter brings value-increasing innovative solutions by providing an improved product or service for which the customer is prepared to pay more. Fig. 2.5 shows a model that illustrates these concepts in the context of a PFI project.

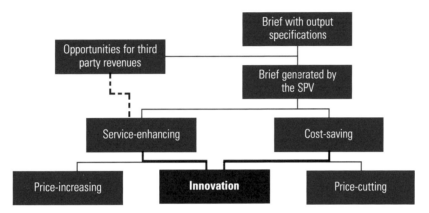

Figure 2.5 *Innovation in the context of PFI*

The opportunities for innovation are seen as originating in the public sector client's output specification. This is interpreted by the PFI company into a series of briefs including, at least, briefs for design and operation. For a PFI proposal to be acceptable it must both offer value for money (VFM) and be affordable by the public sector client. Therefore, although the option is present to enhance the service, the focus of attention will be expected to be on reducing costs.

An additional consideration to bear in mind is that throughout the whole report, cost savings are defined as cost savings over the project life-cycle. More exactly, they are the anticipated savings, discounted to present value, over the duration of the PFI contract. Thus, they include quality improvements aimed to increase durability, reduce running costs or reduce revenue losses from non-availability of service. Moreover, improvements in the built facility intended to reduce costs of providing the service are treated as cost saving innovations (CSIs). And, although this work is focused on those innovations that result in cost saving to the PFI process, relevant product-enhancing innovations related to third party revenues were also considered and examined.

Finally, a clarification is needed in order to ensure that the concepts used throughout the report are not misunderstood. The differences between process, product and services were considered, in the PFI context, to be as illustrated in Fig. 2.6.

Innovation and competition

There has to be an element of temporary competitive advantage on the part of an innovating firm over its rivals, to allow the construction and/or operating cost savings necessary to recoup and obtain a return on the costs invested in developing the innovation. If those 'investment' costs are small relative to the value of the cost saving

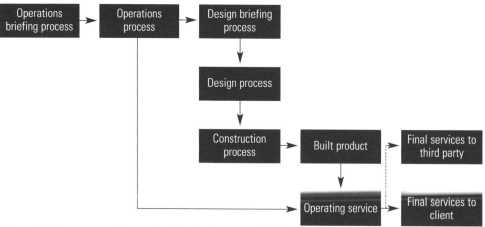

Figure 2.6 *Processes, products and services in the context of PFI*

obtained in the PFI project on which the innovation is first developed and applied, the period of temporary advantage may need to be no longer than the duration of the contract-award process for the single project. However, as we move from left to right along the axis shown in Fig. 2.4, the 'investment cost' of the innovation will tend to increase. Therefore, radical, system, architectural and even modular innovations become less likely the smaller the size of the PFI project, unless such investment cost can be recouped over a stream of projects. For this to happen, the investor in innovation has to be confident that:

- there will be sufficient future clients with appropriate PFI projects on which their innovation can be applied
- by the time such projects appear on the market, the innovator will still retain their competitive advantage over rivals; that is, that their innovation will not have become public knowledge and been widely copied.

On the other hand, the public sector client will benefit from innovation to the extent that competition, and potential imitation of the innovation, forces the cost saving achieved to be passed on as lower prices.

2.4 Inhibitors and enablers – in four steps

Step 1

Using our simple model of the search for CSIs as an investment-like activity undertaken by rational profit-seeking firms, we were able to generate several hypotheses concerning factors that we would expect to act as inhibitors or enablers, all based on ideas of *incentive* and *opportunity* to innovate.

We hypothesised that the amount of CSI would be a function of the amount of expenditure (including expenditure of time and effort) on the search for CSIs that PFI firms found it rational to undertake; and that the latter would in turn be a function of:

(a) the strength and forms of the profit incentives created by the particular form of the PFI contract

(b) the extent to which other incentives, not focusing on CSIs, were (perhaps inadvertently) created by the PFI contract

(c) the extent to which the factors affecting the cost/value ratio were themselves functions of the amount and quality of 'effort' expended by the PFI company, and not functions of factors outside its control

(d) the cost to the firm of acquiring the expertise and knowledge required to search for, to find and then to implement a CSI

(e) the effect of CSI-seeking expenditures on the dispersion of possible outcomes, as well as on their 'most likely' outcome

(f) the attitude to risk (risk aversion or neutrality) of the PFI company

(g) the scope of the contract, measured by value and content

(h) the scope of the contract, measured by completeness of the service, and the extent and complexity of interfaces between the PFI provider and the provider of final services

(i) the effect of contractual arrangements between the PFI company and its suppliers.

Some of the risk issues ((c) and (e)), we hypothesised, would differ most in their effects between projects where the PFI contract included 'volume' or 'demand' risk and ones where it did not. Prior knowledge of contract contents enabled us to identify transport and some accommodation and utilities projects as containing most demand risk.

The 'cost-of-knowledge' issues ((d)), we hypothesised, would differ most in their effects between projects where the range of activities required by the PFI contract were previously the specialisms of several separate companies and those where one company already possessed most of the necessary competencies. We took road projects to be an instance of the latter.

Some of the scope issues ((g) and (h)), we hypothesised, would differ most in their effects between, on the one hand, large and 'complete service' PFI projects such as prisons, and on the other small and 'partial service' projects such as many of those found in the education sector.

This modelling of the search for CSIs as an investment expenditure would predict different outcomes for cases where that investment must be relatively large and where it need not. This, we hypothesised, would not only differentiate between Incremental and other kinds of innovation, but also perhaps between 'technologically based' and other sources of innovation.

Step 2

Onto this simple model, we then added hypotheses based on the use of *transaction cost economics*. Transactions, such as the procurement of a facility and a service, differ one from another in a range of dimensions, called *transaction attributes*. These concern such things as:

- the size of the transaction
- the frequency (or repetition) of the transaction
- the uncertainty of the client's requirements
- the specificity of the client's requirements
- the complexity of the task of meeting those requirements
- the ease with which the deliverables (outputs) can be measured
- the ease with which inputs to the production of the output can be monitored
- the 'atmosphere' (conducive to trust, or otherwise) within which the transaction occurs.

Transaction cost economics identifies a range of modes of organisation of transactions, often called *governance structures* (Williamson, 1985). These range from the pure 'spot' or short-term contract market mode at one pole, to full vertical integration of the organisations requiring to transact at the other. It predicts that, relatively, each governance structure will be more or less efficient than others as a means of governing transactions with certain attributes.

In particular, the problems arising from transaction-specificity of assets (asset-specificity, for short) have to be overcome. A mode of governance 'fails' if there are potentially mutually beneficial ('efficient') investments that are not made because the two parties concerned cannot come to a 'cooperative' solution. Specifically, they need to solve the potential 'hold-up' problem. Once committed to an irreversible 'investment', which means simply a future-orientated expenditure of any kind which has a lower value in its best alternative use outside the particular transaction, i.e. asset-specificity, a party is vulnerable to an opportunistic re-negotiation strategy by the other party. Fearing this, unless some suitable form of protection or guarantee can be devised, the party may refuse to make the investment, and thus potential efficiency gains are lost. Vertical integration and long-term contracting may, each in certain specified circumstances, solve such 'hold-up problems' better than short-term contracting.

The switch to PFI from 'traditional' public sector practices of separate contracts for design and construction with private sector parties, followed by in-house operation of the facility by the public sector's own employees, changes governance structures and transaction attributes in two major ways.

On the one hand, it increases the size, uncertainty and complexity, but reduces the frequency, of the public sector's transactions; whilst at the same time switching from a vertical integration governance structure for operating services to one of long-term contracting.

On the other hand, from the perspective of a former private sector contractor to the public sector moving into the role of a PFI company, it replaces short-term contracts to design and / or construct a specified facility by long-term contracts to supply a service, and creates the potential (though not the requirement) for the PFI company to itself vertically integrate all the activities required to provide that service.

This transaction cost perspective led us to explore the extent to which potentially efficient investments in asset-specificity were not occurring under the 'traditional' contractual arrangements. The implementation of such investments, after the switch to PFI, would then appear as a series of CSIs.

At the same time, the greater complexity and uncertainty of the content of PFI transactions would be hypothesised to create greater 'protection costs' of transactions, as parties sought to write 'complete' contracts under conditions where this would be very difficult and costly (see Section 2.5 below). We sought to measure this effect by examining the legal and associated fees found in PFI compared with traditional arrangements.

The factor of 'frequency' of transactions is closely associated with the value of the 'reputation' of each party to a transaction in the eyes of its co-transactor. This, we hypothesised, would generate significant differences between PFI projects that were part of the programmes of 'repeat' clients and others.

The factors of uncertainty and complexity, and the difficulty of 'complete contracting', would be revealed by differences in the results of, and the process of writing, output specifications.

The extent to which previous arrangements had prevented efficient investments in asset-specificity would, we hypothesised, depend both on the underlying 'technology' of the facility and service, and on the former procurement routines in use. Each of these was likely to vary significantly between projects of different functional types and between projects with different types of client.

Step 3

Next, we adopted an approach in which the search for innovation is seen as a *boundedly-rational search* for profit opportunities, conducted under severe constraints of information availability and of time. We posited that the boundedly-rational response to such constraints would be to implement search heuristics (rules-of-thumb), designed to focus and time-limit such searches; and that the directions of search would be steered by 'common sense knowledge' (i.e. preconceived and informationally-limited notions) of areas of opportunity for cost saving. We posited that the directions for search indicated by such factors would differ significantly between types of organisation, and would be influenced by which type of organisation 'led' the PFI consortium.

Step 4

Finally, we adopted a model of *organisational learning and competence*, taken from recent management literature and from 'evolutionary' economics. This predicts that organisations of the same 'kind' will differ in their competencies, and thus in their abilities to procure and provide efficiently and innovatively; and that these differences will be both path-dependent, that is based on the experience of the organisation and its members, and cultural, that is based on the organisation's ability to learn from its experiences.

This led us to predict differences in CSI between experienced and inexperienced participants, and between 'learning organisations' and others.

2.5 The nature of PFI contracts

Modern economics considers contracts to be a means of coping with the problems facing transactions raised by opportunism and lack of information.

In the absence of opportunism, a *promise* would be as good as a contract. In particular, each party could promise to agree a 'reasonable' adjustment of responsibilities and entitlements in the light of whatever unforeseen circumstances might arise during the performance of the transaction. Contracts are made necessary because, given the risk that some transactors will behave opportunistically, it is not safe to rely on any transactor keeping to such a promise.

Opportunism here means a transactor who pursues self-interest, using concealment or 'guile', and is prepared to breach promises to pursue a shared interest if it is in the transactor's own self-interest to do so.

If one transactor cannot observe the actions of the other, it is necessary to devise a contract which (as far as possible) 'aligns incentives' and ties the reward of the other to achievement of the outcome desired by the first party.

Here the contract is a device to solve a problem of information asymmetry. Transactor B possesses full information about its own actions, but transactor A cannot obtain this information. Full alignment of incentives by means of contract may then be impossible to achieve.

In the presence of risk of opportunism, ideally contracts should be *complete*. That is, they should specify responsibilities and entitlements of each party under each contingent set of conditions that *may* arise during the performance of the contract. However, where the duration of contracts is long and the future is difficult to predict, it becomes absolutely impossible to make contracts complete (some contingencies are not foreseen) and very costly even to achieve coverage of all foreseen contingent possibilities.

Because PFI contracts are of such long duration, they must necessarily be *incomplete*, to the degree to which we cannot draw up, in advance, a complete set of clauses dealing with every set of circumstances that might arise. Even if we could, it would be very costly to do so.

"Complete contracts anticipate every possible state of the world, with fully defined sequences following each outcome. Unless monitoring and enforcement are both possible, there is little point in forming such a detailed agreement ... Complete contracts are costly to draw up ... then there follow the costs involved in monitoring the many provisions of the contract in the light of subsequent outcomes" (Munford, 1998, p.101)

and

"Contracts can be classified according to the degree of completeness that they embody, and ... how far the parties are prepared to accept ambiguities and possible causes of disagreement that will arise in future. The greater the trust on all sides, the less trouble has to be taken beforehand to anticipate difficulties" (Munford, 1998, p.111).

Since trust is the key to incomplete contracting, it is important to eliminate as far as possible the danger of contracting with a party who may behave opportunistically. The prospect of a mutually advantageous future contract, which would be lost if trust were breached, is one main way of increasing each party's ability to trust the other.

Chapter 3

Project managers' subjective measurements and opinions

Synopsis

Data was gathered on 67 PFI projects from 108 expert and highly informed respondents. These respondents were fairly evenly divided between the public (43%) and the private sectors (57%). In each case, the respondent was the organisation's manager of that particular project. This is the biggest survey of this nature undertaken to date of PFI project managers. It is particularly novel in its inclusion of private sector respondents (from special purpose vehicles (SPVs) and their principal suppliers).

The median reported total DBO cost saving is in the range 5–10%. Reported savings are highest (median in the range 10–20%) in custodial and transport projects and lowest (median in the range 5% saving to 5% increase) for education and healthcare projects.

There were significant differences in views on the inefficiency of traditional procurement between respondents managing different types of project. Transport, accommodation and housing pre-PFI procurement is regarded as relatively more efficient, and custodial as less efficient.

Innovations in civil engineering PFI projects are reported to be mainly technological, whereas those in building PFI projects are mainly innovations in business processes, and are less frequently technologically based. The most typical forms of PFI technological innovation involve standardisation of designs, prefabrication and equipment-for-labour substitution in operations. Key innovations were typically developed in early and still competitive stages of the project processes.

The output specifications (OS) used were described by private sector (SPV) respondents as still at least in part 'technical' on over 40% of PFI projects, but were only rarely (12% of projects) so described by the public sector respondents. Only one-quarter of the SPV respondents rated the clients' OS as 'highly appropriate'. Centralised clients (e.g. Highways Agency, MoD, HM Prison Service) reported much less difficulty in writing and less dissatisfaction with their OS than did decentralised clients.

The vast majority of the respondents regarded risk allocation achieved on projects between public and private sectors as appropriate. The value of risk transfer (and costs of risks assumed) was reported to comprise mostly demand and construction risk in the case of civil engineering projects and operation risk in the case of building projects.

In less than half of all projects, and very few projects of decentralised clients, were clients able to make VFM comparison with, and to select between, the PFI solution and a conventionally-funded solution providing a similar level of service.

3.1 Introduction

This chapter reports the results of an extensive questionnaire survey of public and private sector PFI project managers about cost saving and innovation in the particular projects for which they were responsible. See Appendix A.1 for a full explanation of survey methodology and Appendix A.3 for discussion of the sample response.

The survey included questions of two broad types. The first type of question aimed to obtain a *subjective measurement* of the extent, type or relative importance of: inputs defining the project process (OS, risk allocation, the organisations involved); the project process itself (time-scale, form of VFM test); and the outputs of the process (cost savings achieved, innovations achieved). Many of these questions asked respondents to differentiate in their answers between areas of the project (e.g. design, construction, operation).

The second type of question aimed to obtain respondents' opinions regarding causes and effects, of both pre-PFI and PFI project outcomes; and regarding the appropriateness or effectiveness of both pre-PFI and PFI processes of procurement and provision.

Table 3.1 summarises the contents of each section of this chapter in terms of the kinds of questions and results reported therein.

Section	Subjective measurements	Opinions
3.2	Areas of the traditionally procured project with the greater scope for CSIs	Efficiency of previous procurement and provision for the same type of project
3.3	Areas of the PFI project with the greater scope for CSIs	—
3.4	Extent of cost savings achieved on the project, broken down by area of saving	—
3.5	Areas of the project in which the most important CSIs were obtained; areas of technology of greatest importance in the project; types and sources of innovation achieved in the project	Why the innovations made in the project had not been made before
3.6	Type of OS used in the project	Appropriateness of the OS used in the project
3.7	Relative importance of each category of risk in the project	Appropriateness of the risk allocation made on the project
3.8	Time-scale of the development process in the project	Effects of size of project on VFM achieved/achievable; suitability of the PFI model to the project
3.9	PFI experience of the respondents' organisation; number, experience and training of staff on the project	Cultural change caused within the organisation by participating in PFI
3.10	Form of the project's PFI VFM tests	—
3.11	—	Most important areas for action to make PFI process more efficient

Table 3.1 *Summary of contents of Chapter 3*

3.2 Inefficiencies in traditional procurement and provision

The questionnaire tried to put the PFI project being addressed into its context. In that sense, it examined opinions on the scope for cost-saving innovations (CSIs) that the traditionally procured project (facility and services) of the same type has, and the degree of inefficiency perceived in the solutions obtained from previous methods of provision. The latter opinion was sought only from public sector clients.

The questionnaire explored the areas in which there was scope for rethinking the procurement and provision process in projects of the same type as the PFI project.

The general responses are shown in Fig. 3.1. It can be seen that there is no obvious focusing on particular areas of expected scope for CSIs. All areas are reported as between 'relevant' and 'very relevant', with the exception of third party revenues. That area obtained high scores in only a few projects due to its specificity.

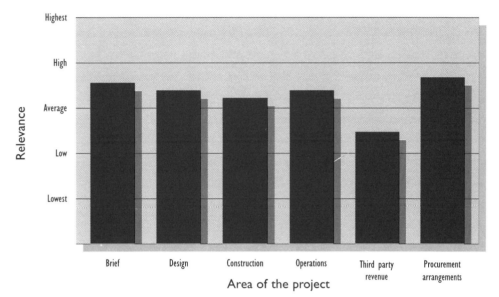

Figure 3.1 *Areas with scope for CSIs in traditionally procured projects of the same type*

If the same answers are classified by type of facility, differences worthy of comment become apparent. As shown in Table 3.2, the briefing and operations processes are seen to have presented particular weaknesses in the custodial sector prior to the introduction of PFI. However, the transport sector reports precisely the opposite. At the same time, both those sectors show a high score in the scope for CSIs in the design and construction processes, for which housing shows the lowest reported scope. With regard to third party revenue, the education and utilities sectors score the highest, while in the other sectors this aspect does not appear to have much relevance. The category 'procurement arrangements' was offered for respondents wishing to indicate that scope lay not in any one of the briefing, design, construction and operation processes, but in the arrangements for interrelating these in the procurement process as a whole, or in the scope for rethinking the process of competition and selection and appointment of suppliers. High overall scores for this factor we interpret as expressing dissatisfaction with the effectiveness of mechanisms of selection, and thus of competition, in traditional procurement.

Type of facility	Brief	Design	Construction	Operations	Third party revenue	Procurement arrangements
Accommodation (non-housing)	4.0	3.5	3.2	3.3	2.6	3.8
Education	3.3	3.0	3.5	3.4	2.9	3.8
Healthcare	3.9	3.8	3.4	3.5	2.6	3.7
Custodial	4.5	3.6	3.5	4.4	2.5	4.0
Housing	3.0	2.8	2.8	3.0	2.0	3.6
Transport	2.6	3.6	3.4	2.9	1.9	3.6
Utilities	3.6	3.1	3.1	3.9	3.8	3.9

Table 3.2 *Average relevance of scope for CSIs in traditionally procured projects*

Overall, the scope for CSIs in all areas is reported as highest for custodial PFIs, and lowest for transport. The transport sector shows a different view of the scope for CSIs to the other sectors. This may reflect some peculiarities both in the way that transport PFIs (mainly, but not solely, DBFO roads) have been constituted as well as a greater emphasis on the part of respondents in the transport sector on the scope for technological/engineering innovations – an issue that will recur throughout this report. The emphasis in this sector is put on the D&B aspects rather than on the briefing or operational aspects. This may be a result of a 'highly technically-focused' sector, in which 'business process' considerations are not as prevalent as in the other sectors (see Section 3.5 Sources and circumstances of innovation and Section 3.7 Risks of the project). It should be borne in mind that, in fact, in most road DBFOs the transformation of brief into an outline design, sufficient to obtain planning permission, has remained the function of the Department of Transport – hence, inevitably, a restriction in scope from 'rethinking the what' to 'rethinking the how'. The lower score given to scope for CSIs in transport operation may, likewise, reflect a general belief that scope for CSIs is greater in other services (largely absent in transport) than in facilities management (FM) (in roads, mainly repair, maintenance, signing and vehicle/user management).

The survey also explored the degree of efficiency attributed by the clients to the procurement process implemented before PFI. The idea was to incorporate into the analysis the fact that a certain sector might be obtaining greater performance in PFI, as a result of improving poor previous management of the process of procurement of facilities and services. From the results shown in Tables 3.3 and 3.4, the custodial sector seems to be one of those cases. On the other hand, healthcare shows the opposite results.

Degree of efficiency	Proportion
Efficient solutions	37%
Moderately inefficient solutions	43%
Highly inefficient solutions	20%

Table 3.3 Degree of efficiency of solutions obtained by PFI clients before procuring PFI projects

Type of facility	Efficient solutions	Moderately inefficient solutions	Highly inefficient solutions
Accommodation (non-housing)	3	3	0
Education	1	0	0
Healthcare	5	2	2
Custodial	0	0	3
Housing	1	1	0
Transport	0	6	0
Utilities	1	1	1
Total building projects	10	6	5
Total civil engineering projects	1	7	1

Table 3.4 Degree of efficiency of the solutions obtained by PFI clients before procuring PFI projects, classified by type of facility

However, the statistical validity of the results is very low, because of the small number of responses (from clients only) in each category. In particular, we can not answer the following question. How much of the efficiency gains reported are attributable to the positive and unique virtues of PFI, and how much to the elimination of inefficiencies that could have been removed in another way?

3.3 Scope for cost saving innovations in the particular PFI project

The survey asked respondents to identify the areas in which there was most scope for innovation to reduce final costs of supply of service in the particular project, given its scope, specification, technical content, etc. The answers were consistent with those in response to the previous question. In general, the categories showing the most relevance were 'improving procurement efficiencies', 'improving quality management', 'improving buildability' and 'improving staff efficiency during operations' (see Fig. 3.2). However, differences in mean scores were not significant. Again, for PFI projects as a whole, we see no obvious strong focus on particular areas. This can be interpreted as indicating that the scope for CSIs is found, if at all, in diverse areas, depending on the specific characteristics of each project.

The custodial sector, for example, shows a consistently higher score on many of the categories (no less than 11 factors, out of a possible 16, have scores of 3.5 or above), suggesting that the scope for innovation, although clearly wider on the operations side, is present in the perception of respondents in most aspects of these projects (see Tables 3.2, 3.5 and Fig. 3.3).

Accommodation projects report an average scope (with scores of 3.5 or above in 5 out of 16 areas). With respect to the operational aspects, the transport sector scores are generally low. The healthcare sector reports slightly higher scope than most sectors for CSIs in operation. Utilities projects report scores generally higher than, say, education or housing, and higher than any other sector in construction aspects. Education and housing scores are low both in operational and construction-related aspects.

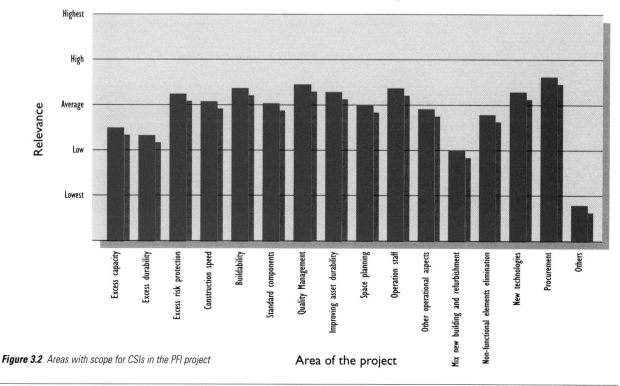

Figure 3.2 *Areas with scope for CSIs in the PFI project*

Type of facility	Excess capacity	Excess durability	Excess of risk protection	Construction speed	Buildability	Standard components	Quality management	Improving asset durability	Space planning	Operation staff	Other operations	Mix new building and refurbishment	Non-functional elements elimination	New technologies (construction and operation)	Procurement	Other
Accommodation (non-housing)	2.9	2.3	3.4	2.7	3.2	2.9	3.2	3.7	3.7	3.3	3.5	2.2	3.1	3.7	3.7	1.0
Education	1.9	1.4	2.6	2.3	3.0	2.6	2.2	2.6	2.5	2.0	2.5	1.7	2.2	2.6	3.3	0.5
Healthcare	2.9	2.5	3.1	3.2	3.3	3.1	3.5	3.6	3.4	3.4	3.2	2.3	2.9	3.1	3.5	0.5
Custodial	3.2	3.3	3.7	3.6	3.8	3.7	3.9	3.5	4.4	4.2	3.6	1.6	3.4	3.7	3.9	0.6
Housing	1.8	1.4	2.4	3.2	2.8	3.2	3.2	3.0	2.2	1.8	2.6	1.6	2.8	3.0	3.8	1.0
Transport	1.6	2.2	3.4	3.2	3.9	2.8	3.7	3.2	1.6	3.4	1.9	2.3	2.3	3.3	3.4	0.9
Utilities	3.0	3.2	3.4	3.4	3.1	3.2	3.0	2.4	2.6	3.6	3.3	2.4	3.3	3.4	4.4	1.7

Table 3.5 *Average relevance of scope for CSIs in the PFI project*

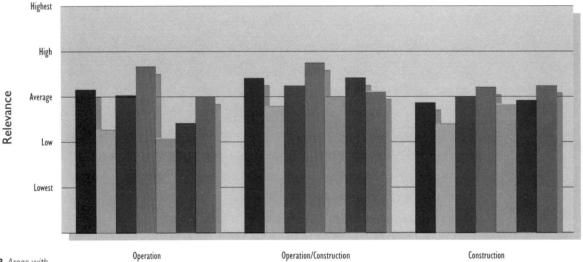

Figure 3.3 *Areas with scope for CSIs in the PFI project – analysis by type of facility*

■ Accomodation non-housing   ■ Education   ■ Healthcare   ■ Custodial   ■ Housing   ■ Transport   ■ Utilities

3.4   Savings achieved in the PFI project

An imperative of the research was to find a way of evaluating the savings actually achieved in the PFI process. This required careful consideration, as savings estimates may be prone to bias, given the subjective nature of the appraisal. At the same time, for reasons derived from our concern to obtain a high response rate, it was essential to reduce as far as possible the time and effort required of a respondent to complete the questionnaire. Therefore we did not ask respondents to report detailed figures. Broad quantitative estimates were requested and the answer format gave numeric range options.

In the main part of the questionnaire in which the valuation of savings was requested, this was done in consideration of the benchmark that each respondent could use. In other words, the following results reflect the respondents' subjective measurement of the quantitative savings in comparison with the public sector comparator (PSC) or VFMC, in the case of public sector respondents, but in comparison with the respondent's own benchmark, in the case of the private sector.

Private sector respondents cannot be presumed to have knowledge of the PSC. Moreover, we wished private sector respondents to compare their submitted costs with their own earlier estimates of a probable or target cost, to reflect their success or failure in finding cost savings, in relation to their own expectations. We took account of the possibility that these initial expectations might not have been fully or formally expressed as single-value figures.

The reduction in data resolution resulting from forming the questions as numeric range options was considered acceptable. It was considered that to attempt to achieve high precision when measuring the cost savings in these projects would certainly have raised the difficulty of obtaining responses, and, at least on the private sector side, would quite probably have proved futile. However, since the interest of the research lies in the measurement of the difference between those reported savings, rather than the actual magnitude of the saving reported in each project, this focus was given to the analysis.

In Fig. 3.4, a series of column charts illustrates the ranges of cost saving or cost increase reported as achieved in each of the stages of cost expense in the PFI project (from preliminary costs to core operations costs and total costs of the project). The column heights represent the frequency of responses in each cost saving range obtained in the survey.

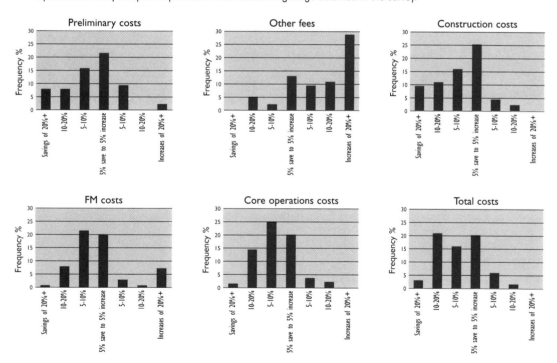

There is a clear tendency towards savings in all the categories, except in other fees, where the modal (most frequent) outcome is clearly a cost increase of 20% or more. If we focus only on the total savings it is possible to conclude that the *median of the reported savings lies in the range 5–10%*. There is no difference in this respect between the savings reported by the public sector and the private sector respondents.

Figure 3.4 Cost savings achieved in the PFI projects, separated by stage

An analysis by sector has been carried out, where the availability of data allowed, and the respective results are shown in similar graphs included in Appendix A.6.

Summary comments on percentage cost savings reported as achieved in each sector follow (see also Appendix A.6).

- *Accommodation.* No savings in construction. Largest savings are in operations and FM. Other fees increases are not as large as in other sectors.
- *Education.* Insufficient responses to draw clear conclusions. However, there is a tendency towards smaller savings in total costs, probably not reaching even 5%. In other fees there is a clear increase. The largest savings are found in operations and FM.
- *Healthcare.* Other fees increases are extremely marked. Slight savings in construction. Highest savings are in operations and FM.
- *Custodial.* The tendency is clearly for total cost savings to be between 10% and 20%. Other fees increases are smaller than in other categories and distributed across the series of ranges.
- *Transport.* Other fees increases are very clear. Most savings are in construction. Savings in operations are around nil. Total savings are between 10% and 20%.

It is possible to infer that the cost increases in the category other fees could be used as an indicator of the (lack of) smoothness of the PFI procurement process. The sectors that have been generally regarded as encountering most difficulties in completing that process are education and healthcare.

The case of roads is a special one, as total savings here may be demonstrating the effect of the eight early road schemes, carried out in two rounds. The savings in transport are essentially in construction costs. This aspect is confirmed in a series of additional analyses in Chapter 4.

3.5 Sources and circumstances of innovation

Figure 3.5 shows the relative importance of the ways in which the CSIs have been generated, or were expected to be generated. Not only are the majority of innovations reported incremental, but such innovations are ranked as being of much greater importance than any other kind. This is not surprising, as incremental innovations are the most common kind of innovation in the construction industry.

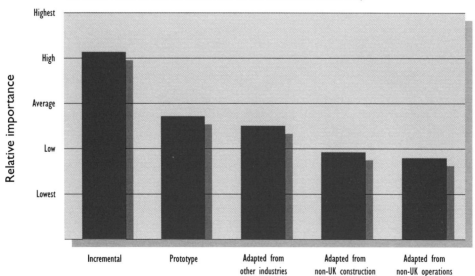

Figure 3.5 *How the CSIs were generated in the PFI project*

Nevertheless, an unexpected result can be found in the relatively high ranking of prototype solutions. This category seems to take a similar importance to the initiatives of re-adapting existing ideas from other industries or countries. A clear explanation of this aspect, however, is to be found in an analysis of responses by sectors given in Table 3.6,

- in all sectors, incremental innovations are the most important
- in building sectors, prototype innovations rank next in importance, with adaptations from abroad the least important
- in civil engineering sectors, adaptations from abroad rank above prototype innovations
- the custodial sector departs from the general pattern for building in giving a higher ranking to adaptation from non-UK operations
- in transport, adaptations from non-UK construction rank next after incremental
- utilities differ from transport in giving a higher rank to adaptations from other industries, and a lower rank to adaptations from abroad
- housing does not contain enough answers to draw clear conclusions.

Type of facility	Incremental	Prototype	Adapted from other industries	Adapted from non-UK construction	Adapted from non-UK operations
Accommodation (non-housing)	3.9	3.0	3.1	2.1	2.4
Education	4.4	3.2	2.6	2.4	1.8
Healthcare	4.5	2.5	2.9	1.7	1.5
Custodial	3.9	3.4	1.9	2.2	2.4
Housing	2.7	4.3	2.3	1.3	1.0
Transport	4.5	2.5	1.7	3.1	2.5
Utilities	4.8	1.9	3.5	1.6	2.1

Table 3.6 Relative importance of the ways of generating CSIs in the PFI project

Proportion of technologically rooted CSIs

Another area of the questionnaire requested information about the proportion of CSIs which had technological roots. The general results, as well as the results grouped by type of facility, are illustrated in Fig. 3.6. The conclusions that can be drawn from this analysis are that the building projects base considerably more of their CSIs on non-technologically rooted initiatives. However, the civil engineering projects, such as roads or utilities, rely heavily on technically based innovations.

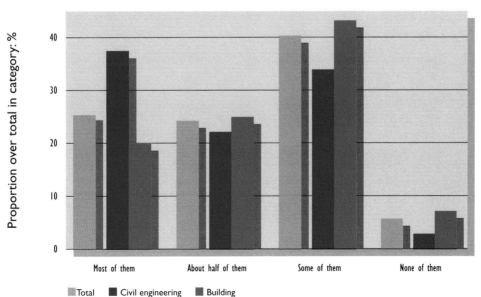

Figure 3.6 Proportion of CSIs with technological roots in the PFI project

If these results are combined with those presented in Section 3.2, it is possible to conclude that the civil engineering projects are essentially improving on the design and construction technical aspects, and doing so in a 'classical' manner, i.e. incrementally improving over the existing practices. When technically rooted CSIs in the civil engineering projects are not merely incremental, they are usually based on existing ideas from other industries or from overseas construction industries. Despite this, the existence of non-technically rooted CSIs in the civil engineering projects cannot be disregarded.

On the other hand, the most significant 'business process' innovations, not based on technological aspects, are being brought forward in the context of building projects. It is within the context of those projects that the new briefs to designers, determination of innovative operation regimes, new FM schemes, and other 'business-based' CSIs take shape most clearly.

Reasons for not implementing CSIs previously

The questionnaire also included two sections on the reasons why the CSIs of the projects were not applied before. The first of those questions explored whether the necessary technical expertise had previously been lacking. The answers were very consistent among the participants in building projects. In the case of transport, the answers were also similar, except for the low score obtained in the category of 'expertise absent from the organisation', where the mean is clearly lower (see Fig. 3.7 and Table 3.7).

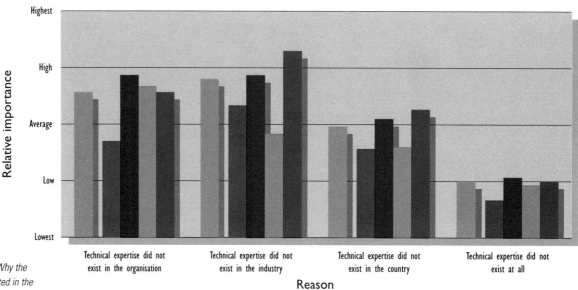

Figure 3.6 *Why the CSIs generated in the PFI project were not implemented previously*

Type of facility	Number of answers to survey	Technical expertise did not exist in the organisation	Technical expertise did not exist in the industry	Technical expertise did not exist in the country	Technical expertise did not exist at all
Accommodation (non-housing)	10	2.9	2.7	2.7	1.7
Education	6	3.2	3.0	2.3	1.5
Healthcare	12	2.8	2.8	1.7	0.8
Custodial	10	3.0	3.3	2.2	0.4
Transport	7	1.0	3.3	2.3	0.4

Table 3.7 *Relative importance of the lack of expertise as reason for the CSIs in the PFI project not to have been implemented previously*

Nevertheless, the rate of response to this question was only 50/108 = 46%. Several respondents thought that the question was not applicable to their cases. It is therefore clear that the CSIs were frequently not applied previously due to reasons other than lack of expertise.

In the cases where the expertise did not exist, it was generally acquired from other organisations or industries, rather than from other countries or being generated from scratch.

The second question investigating why the CSIs were not applied previously looked for contractual reasons. The answers emphasise 'organisational ways of doing things that inhibited the application of CSIs' and 'weak incentives to innovate', rather than 'norms, or technical codes', or 'contractual arrangements or bargaining with third parties' (see Fig. 3.8). It therefore seems to be the case that the contractual environment was inhibiting the generation of CSIs. Thus barriers to innovations were not necessarily external to the participant organisations, but were to be found in contracts devised by those organisations or in the internal business cultures and routines of the organisations themselves.

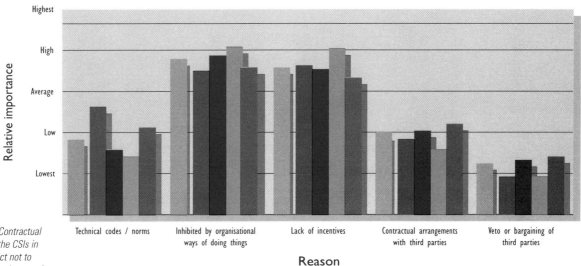

Figure 3.8 Contractual reasons for the CSIs in the PFI project not to have been implemented previously

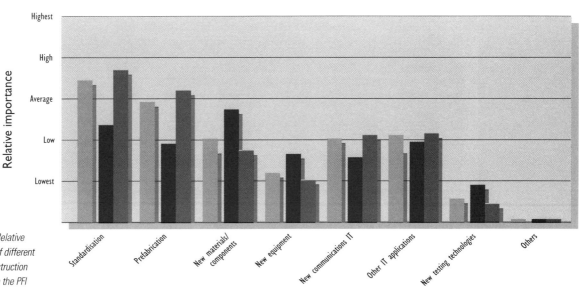

Figure 3.9 Relative importance of different areas of construction technology in the PFI project

Types of technologically rooted CSIs

Another pair of questions explored the relevance of different areas of construction and operations technology. The results in respect of construction technology again clearly differ between the building and the civil engineering projects. The former put the emphasis on standardisation and pre-fabrication, while the latter focus on the use of new materials, new components, new equipment or new testing techniques (see Fig. 3.9)

Differences between the building and civil engineering sectors in the results for the relative importance of different areas of operations technology are slight (see Fig. 3.10). Except for the differences in the scope for the substitution of personnel by new equipment, both sectors seem to follow similar tactics at the moment to improve the efficiency of the operations process.

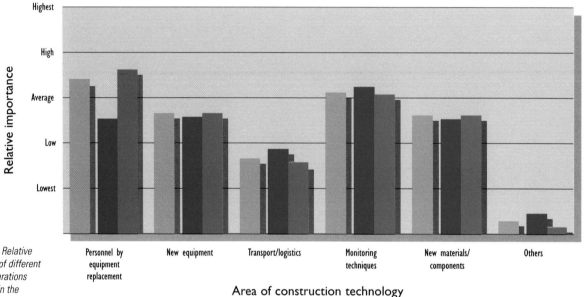

Figure 3.10 *Relative importance of different areas of operations technology in the PFI project*

■ Total   ■ Civil engineering projects   ■ Building projects

The most significant single CSIs

In relation to the most significant individual CSI implemented, or expected to be implemented, in the PFI project – an open question included in the survey – the respondents pointed to a long series of initiatives. The summary of them is shown in Table 3.8.

Application area of the CSI	Frequency
Procurement (Output specifications, contract arrangements, risk transfer, business opportunities)	12
Construction (Design technology and approach, construction technologies and equipment, avoidance of cost and time overruns during construction period)	33
Operations and maintenance (Core operations regime, operating technologies, staff efficiency gains, maintenance schemes and others)	15
Space planning and facilities portfolio (Reduction of floor area, economies of scale when managing several facilities or merging them, better utilisation of space capacity and others)	13
Total	73

Table 3.8 *The most significant single CSIs in the PFI project*

It is notable that the most frequently cited CSIs appear to be construction-related, despite the fact that the technical variety of the solutions is large. However, the most important construction-related CSIs have two main objectives in common: to assure the avoidance of cost and time overruns during the construction period; and to generate a more operationally-driven design of the facility. Aside from construction-related CSIs, application of innovations to find savings in space planning and maintenance costs seem to be the most common most significant single CSIs.

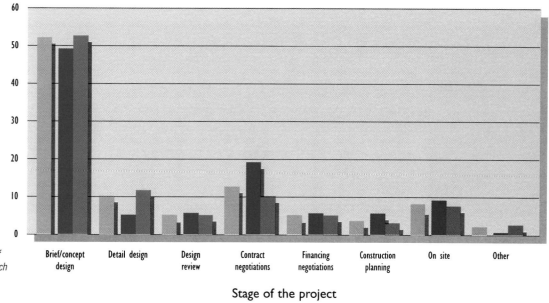

Figure 3.11 *Stage of the PFI project at which the chief CSI was granted*

The questionnaire sought to identify the stage of the project at which the most significant CSI was generated. The results of that enquiry are shown in Fig. 3.11. This figure shows the importance of the very early stages of the project, suggesting that the emphasis is correctly being placed on the stage at which most opportunities for significant improvement arise.

If the separate results for the building and civil engineering sectors are compared, as shown in Fig. 3.11, it is possible to conclude that the behaviour of the building and civil engineering sectors is very similar. However, in building, the detail design and, in civil engineering, the contract negotiation appear to be crucial as stages at which key innovations are generated.

3.6 Output specifications

It is held to be one of the most fundamental 'principles' of PFI (HM Treasury, 1991; Private Finance Panel, 1996) that 'prescriptive' and 'restrictive' specifications of a required facility are thereby simply replaced by specifications of the final outputs (services) required from the facility, leaving as much scope as possible for innovative ways of meeting the service requirement.

The research investigated the composition and importance of the output specifications (OS). First, it explored the characteristics of the OS and the way in which they were generated. Second, we looked at the relationship between the rate of success of projects (as measured by their reported percentage total cost saving) and the design of the OS. The first area is discussed in this section. The latter is considered in Chapter 4.

The first step was to classify the size of the documentation, taking size as a proxy for degree of prescriptiveness. The results of the enquiry are shown in Table 3.9.

Unfortunately, the number of usable responses was not as high as desirable – only 41 different projects, out of a total sampled of 67.

Size of the documentation	Number of cases
Small (<= 200 pages, approx.)	12
Medium (>200 and <500 pages, approx.)	16
Large (> 500 pages, approx.)	13
Total	41

Table 3.9 *Size of the output specifications documentation of the PFI project*

Figure 3.12 shows the principal authors of the OS – as a result of a question that requested identification of the pair of actors that had the greatest participation in the task. In general, the awarding authorities generate their own OS documentation, with a strong component of input from advisers. The participation of final users and PFI/PPP units of the respective government department is also found. However, although the extensive use of the TTF/4Ps/PFPE guidance is recognised by the clients in preliminary stages of the project, they do not appear as direct contributors to the OS.

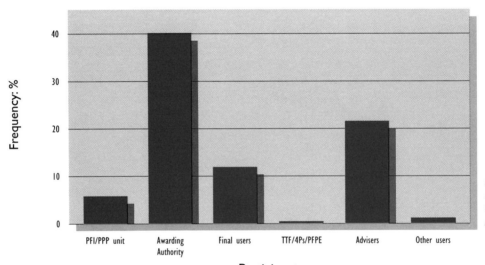

Figure 3.12 *Two most important participants in the writing of the PFI project output specification*

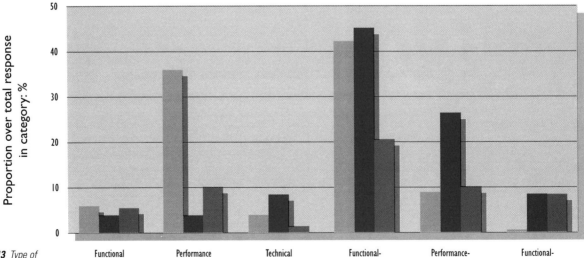

Figure 3.13 *Type of specifications provided in the PFI project*

It was also of interest to the enquiry to establish the type of OS being used in the sampled PFI projects. The Treasury has issued specific guidance in order to encourage the use of functional and/or performance OS.

The results of the enquiry are illustrated in Fig. 3.13, which separates the responses from clients, SPVs and SPV suppliers respectively. The specifications referred to by the last group are, of course, those received from the SPVs rather than the original OS supplied by the client of the project.

We can observe a difference of opinion between the clients and the SPVs, in respect to both their general responses (see Fig. 3.14) and their opinions on the same set of OS (see Fig. 3.15). Fig. 3.15 presents a set of answers relating to the same eleven projects, and thus the same OS, for eleven pairs of clients and SPVs. The outcome is that the SPVs see the actual OS produced by clients as much more technical, and less functional, than the clients do.

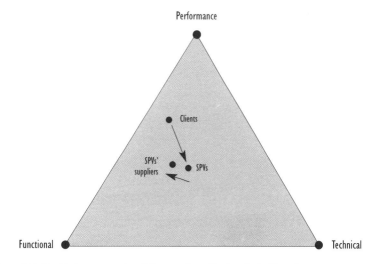

Figure 3.14 *Graphical representation of the type of specifications in the PFI project*

Considering the information supplied to the SPV suppliers, it can be seen that they usually receive much more input than the OS produced by the client. This means that the SPVs are usually incorporating new elements of brief or design, before passing sections of the OS to their suppliers (see Table 3.10).

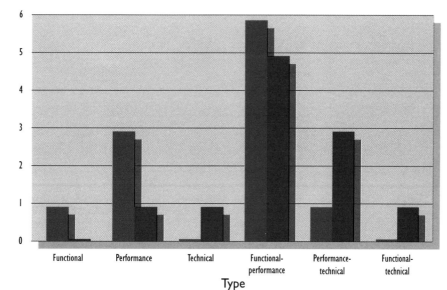

Figure 3.15 *Types of output specifications in a sample of PFI projects*

Type of facility	Information supplied to SPVs' suppliers by the SPV
Only output specifications	3
Output specifications plus some additional information	10
Output specifications plus much other additional information	9
Essentially specially prepared information	4

Table 3.10 *Information content in specifications for SPV suppliers*

Preliminary designs

Preliminary designs may be developed by the public sector and supplied to PFI bidders for one of two quite different reasons. In some projects, this preliminary design constitutes a set of parameters within which the bidder must develop their solution. Such is the case, for instance, in many road DBFOs. In other projects, the design merely provides a potential reference point, which the bidder can either ignore or take as their starting point from which to explore changes.

We explored the extent to which a previously prepared preliminary design had been developed for the client prior to the point of invitation of tenders. Nearly half, 45%, of the respondents said that such designs did exist in the PFI projects in which they were involved. Asked for their view on whether having such a design would help in the bidding process, the majority of respondents, between 55% in the public sector and 82% in the private sector, considered that the supply of such documentation would not have made the process shorter, easier, clearer, cheaper or more accountable.

Figure 3.16 illustrates the influence that the existence of preliminary designs can have. This graph shows the relationship between the types of innovation most typically generated in two different groups of projects: those with a preliminary design and those without one. The frequencies have been normalised in each category, in order to make the visualisation easier.

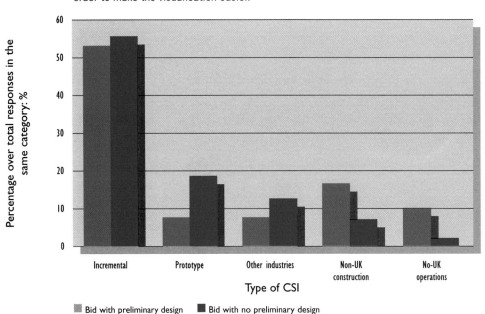

Figure 3.16 *Most important types of CSIs versus existence of preliminary design*

The existence of a preliminary design correlates negatively with the generation of a higher proportion of prototype CSIs and positively with the adaptation of CSIs from abroad. It may be interpreted that the non-existence of preliminary designs is boosting the 'uniqueness' of the solutions implemented in the respective project. However, it is also possible that these results merely reflect the strong association of existence of a preliminary design with certain project types, which in turn are those least likely to feature 'prototype' innovations.

Evaluation of the output specifications

The results of the evaluation of the appropriateness of the OS are illustrated in Table 3.11. These show the judgement of the private participants concerning the appropriateness of the specifications they received, that is, the client OS in the case of the SPVs, and the SPVs' specifications in the case of the SPV suppliers. Both cases reflect a certain discomfort that translates into a most common answer that specifications were only 'moderately appropriate'. Only one quarter (6 out of 23) of SPVs rated the client's OS as highly appropriate, compared to half (16 out of 31) of SPV suppliers rating of SPVs' specifications.

Appropriateness	Answers of SPVs	Answers of SPV suppliers	Total
Absolutely appropriate	2	4	6
Very appropriate	4	12	16
Moderately appropriate	15	14	29
Barely appropriate	1	1	2
Not appropriate at all	1	0	1
Total	23	31	54

Table 3.11 *Appropriateness of the specifications received*

The contradictory points of view between clients and SPVs regarding the extent to which clients had achieved a 'functional' or 'performance' specification, and the low SPV rating of the 'appropriateness' of OS, is perhaps to be expected. SPVs clearly for the most part wish for as free a hand as possible, but perhaps inevitably may tend to underestimate the difficulties faced by clients in trying to avoid 'technical' specifications.

There are likely to be cases where the client has good as well as bad reasons for writing a prescriptive specification. Consider a person trying to specify their own requirements for breakfast. If they have no strong particular preferences, they may find it relatively easy to do this in 'functional' terms ('served at such a time'; 'containing *x* calories, proteins, etc.'). But if what they really want is 'two boiled eggs, still slightly runny, with hot white toast and melted, salted butter', it is easier by far to ask for it directly than to try to write a 'functional' specification in such a way as to ensure that their requirements will be met. Users are more likely than professional procurement agents to possess such strong and specific preferences and requirements. The more involved that users themselves become in the writing of the output specification, the more likely perhaps that 'technical' elements will enter the specification, especially perhaps if a few users dominate the consultation. While all economists would agree that users' preferences should 'count', in addition to cost differences, problems arise in determining which users' preferences, and in particular how future users' preferences, might be taken into account.

Moreover, even in the absence of clearly understood specific preferences or requirements, the very novelty of the process of OS writing might mean that clients find them difficult to produce effectively.

The process of generating the output specifications

In view of the potential problems outlined above, we sought to identify where clients experience most difficulty in writing a 'functional' OS, and why. The questionnaire requested clients and their advisers to identify the factors that were the cause of difficulty in writing the OS. The results of that enquiry are presented in Table 3.12.

Reason	Average relevance
Time period of the PFI contract	3.0
Complexity of the project	3.1
Excessive demand upon the client's team	2.7
Prior experience in PFI	3.0
Legal and technical constraints	2.6
External approvals	2.4
Interfaces between existing and new facilities	2.3
Procurement constraints	1.5

Table 3.12 *Reasons for dissatisfaction when writing the output specifications – answers from clients and their advisers*

Although the differences between average degrees of relevance of the explanatory factors are not great, the experience of the client's team, time scale and complexity of the project appear as the most relevant sources of difficulty. However, if the results are separated by type of client (centralised versus decentralised), and we focus only on the higher evaluations ('very relevant' and 'crucial') then, with the results normalised within each category, the outcome is as shown in Fig. 3.17.

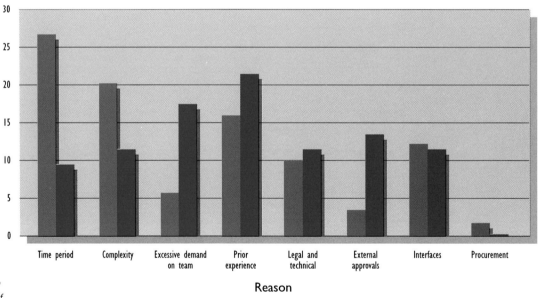

Figure 3.17 *Most important reasons for dissatisfaction with the outputbspecifications of the PFI project – by type of client*

Figure 3.17 highlights two main aspects:

(a) uncertainties arising from the long duration and the complexity of the projects are the key difficulties that a centralised client has to overcome

(b) the demand placed upon an inexperienced team and the need to obtain external approvals are the key issues for a decentralised client.

Our findings do not prove that more 'functional' or 'performance' types of output specification would be entirely advantageous, given the need to balance private sector scope to innovate with appropriateness of specifications to the public sector client's requirements. However, our findings do suggest that if a further shift in that direction is desired by policy makers, there is an issue concerning the kind of support that decentralised client organisations, such as local authorities, will require in order to achieve this effectively.

3.7 Risks of the project

The research investigated risk in the project, initially through a simple question that requested respondents to indicate how the allocation of risks between the public and private sectors was made in the project. The answers to that question are shown in Table 3.13.

Opinion	Proportion (total responses): %	Proportion (responses from public sector participants and their advisers):%	Proportion (responses from private sector participants):%
Too much risk being borne by the client	0	0	0
Adequate balance of risks between the two parties	84	91	78
Too much risk being borne by the SPV	11	7	15
Far too much risk being borne by the SPV	5	2	7

Table 3.13 Opinions on the allocation of risk between public and private sector in the PFI project

It can be seen that the large majority of respondents consider that the balance of risks is adequate between the public and the private sectors. Moreover, the results are similar if analysed by size of the project (Fig. 3.18) and by type of respondent (Table 3.13).

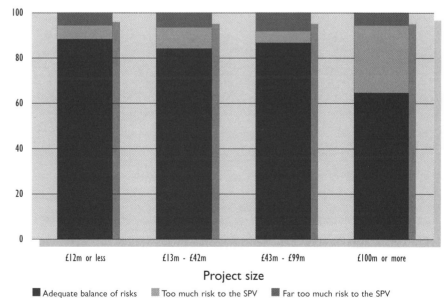

Figure 3.18 Opinion about the allocation of risks between public and private sector in the PFI project – separated by size of the project

Only two comments need to be made in relation to this part of the survey. First, in Fig. 3.18, only in the case of very large projects is there an increase in the proportion of respondents that consider too much risk is being borne by the SPV. Second, Table 3.15 shows a slight difference between the views of the private and the public sector respondents, as to whether too much risk is being borne by the SPV. However, in neither of the two cases are the differences sufficiently significant to draw clear conclusions.

In particular, the respondents who think that the risks transferred by the public sector to the SPV are too great are just seven in number: two clients, four SPVs and one FM adviser to the SPV. Two of these seven are from the transport sector, two are from utilities, two are from accommodation (non-housing) and one from healthcare. It seems probable that the particular risks in question may be demand or 'volume' risks.

Risk aversion of the participants

We asked each respondent to classify not only their own organisation but also each of the other organisations involved in the same project, in terms of 'degree of willingness to accept risks', hereafter termed degree of risk aversion. Figure 3.19 represents the evaluations that the four different types of respondent made of the risk aversion of the different participants in the project.

There is a first very clear point arising from the analysis: the most risk adverse participants are seen by all to be the financiers, scoring over 4 in a scale of 1 to 5. The clients, on the other hand, are evaluated in second place, even by themselves. The participants seen as having the most willingness to bear risks are the operators, contractors and SPVs.

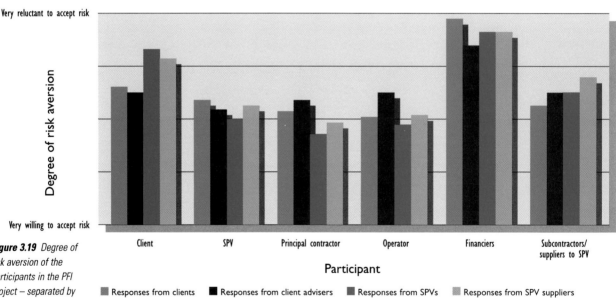

Figure 3.19 Degree of risk aversion of the participants in the PFI project – separated by type of respondent

With regard to the type of clients (it is not only the clients themselves who were being questioned here), it is worth noting that their total scores by type (as awarded by all participants) are:

- centralised clients: 3.8 (general), 4.1 (as considered by private participants)
- decentralised clients: 3.3 (general), 3.5 (as considered by the private participants).

Thus, there is a clear tendency to perceive the experienced and 'repeat' clients, in general, as being more risk averse in their attitudes.

Relevance of different groups of risk in the bids' risk adjustment

From Fig. 3.20 it can be seen that risk adjustments in civil engineering projects are much more concerned with construction and demand aspects, while the risk adjustment on building projects concentrates on operations and performance. The focus of the risk assessment and management is therefore on completely different areas.

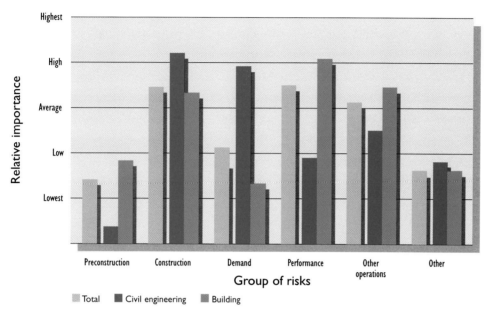

Figure 3.20 *Relative importance of the different groups of risks included in the risk adjustment of the PFI project bid*

3.8 Specific characteristics of the project

Suitability of the PFI model to the project

The first results worthy of comment are those related to the suitability of the PFI procurement model to the particular project. From an examination of Fig.3.21, it is possible to infer that a large majority of the respondents – 81% of them – thinks that the PFI procurement is suitable or very suitable for their project. Moreover, this situation is the same regardless of the type of respondent.

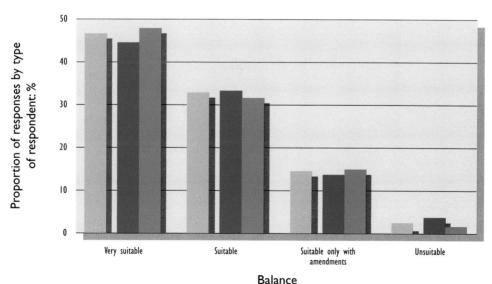

Figure 3.21 *Opinion about the suitability of the PFI procurement model for the PFI project*

However, it is important to remember that the sample is drawn exclusively from projects that have been signed, and, therefore, are at the construction stage, or even in operation. Is it then valid to ask why there is almost 20% of respondents who think that the procurement route required amendments or even that it was unsuitable? It is therefore of interest to ask: who constitutes that 20% and why they think as they do?

Figure 3.22 groups these answers by size of project. The additional information that can be drawn is that 77%, 82%, 90% and 76% of the respondents in each quartile of the size distribution think that the procurement is suitable or very suitable for their project, respectively. In other words, the criticism is somewhat more likely to come from very small or very large projects. Criticism is essentially focused on the need for amendments, rather than on PFI being totally unsuitable.

Further analysis of the responses that are critical indicates that there is no particular type of respondent who is most prone to criticise. Negative opinion on suitability of PFI to the project comes from: 7 clients, 2 SPVs, 2 client advisers, 2 designers, 2 contractors, 1 operator and 3 SPV advisers. These are 19 different people participating in 18 different projects, including accommodation (non-housing), healthcare, education, prisons, housing, utilities and transport, i.e. every classification of facility that the research has used. Interestingly, some of these respondents are reporting on projects that have been awarded prizes for representing examples of innovation and good practice.

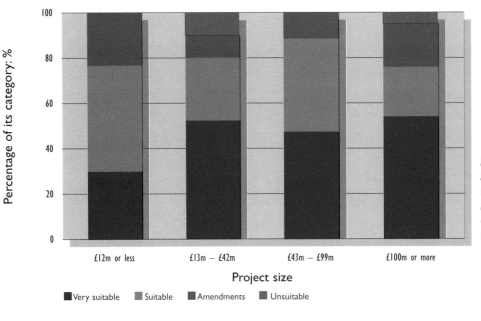

Figure 3.22 *Opinion about the suitability of the PFI procurement model for the PFI project – separated by size of the project*

Size of the project

A factor that is traditionally raised when discussing the characteristics of PFI projects and their appropriateness for PFI is their size. We asked respondents to indicate whether, in their view, the size of the project was likely to have had adverse effects on the value for money (VFM) achieved. The general results to this question are illustrated in Table 3.14.

Opinion	Proportion (total responses): %
Project was too small	7
Project was of an adequate size	73
Project was too large	1
Size has nothing to do with VFM	19

Table 3.14 *Opinion on the influence of the size of the PFI project on value for money achieved*

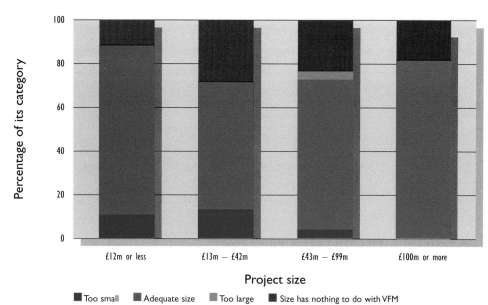

Figure 3.23 *Opinion about the effects of the size of the PFI project on the value for money achieved*

It is of interest to investigate how the answers to this question change with the different respondents, and the project in which they were participating. This analysis is shown in Fig. 3.23. It is seen that 14% of the respondents from the two smaller project size quartiles impute size of the project as having a negative effect for them. However, in any category the most common answer is that the projects were of an adequate size. What is also worth highlighting is the difference in appreciation of the category 'size has nothing to do with VFM'. It seems that as the project gets larger, this response becomes more likely, although it does not account for 25% of the opinions even on large projects. The opinion that a particular project was too large to give VFM under PFI was virtually absent.

It is therefore possible to conclude that the size of the project is a factor that seems to affect the appreciation of VFM achieved in the project. It is, however, a factor of a weaker influence than is generally considered to be the case (by industry's representatives and specialised publications, for example). Indeed, even within the smallest projects, over two-thirds of the respondents considered that the project was of adequate size to achieve VFM potential. This point is discussed again in Chapter 4, with regard to the correlation between the size of the PFI projects and the achievement of cost savings. The conclusion drawn here is consistent with the results that will be presented in the next chapter.

Time-scale of the PFI process

One of the additional results of the survey is the characterisation of the time-scale of the process in a small sub-sample of PFI projects. Those results are illustrated in Fig. 3.24. By itself, this is not a very novel finding, as most of the participants in PFI are already aware of how tight is the typical time-scale for the process. The real value added can be found in the results shown in Fig. 3.25. In this case, for the same projects, the level of design accomplished is illustrated at two key milestones: financial close and start of works on site.

There are clear differences between building and civil engineering projects. In the building projects in this sample, typically 50% of the total amount of design has been carried out by the time of financial close. More than half of the sample of building projects show more than 75% of the design being completed by the time of start of works on site. In contrast, the civil engineering projects show an average of slightly over 25% of the design carried out by the time of financial close, and around 50% at start of works on site.

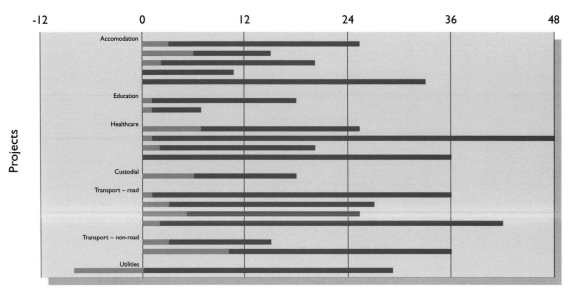

Figure 3.24 *Construction timescale for a smple of PFI projects*

Time: months

■ Financial close to start of works on site   ■ Start of works on site to commissioning

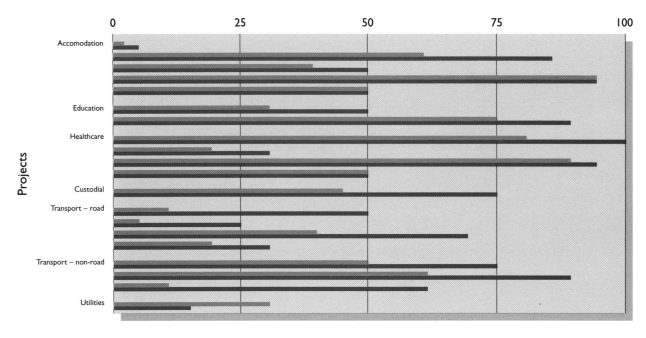

Figure 3.25 *Amount of detail design carried out at financial close and start of works on site in a sample of PFI projects*

Detail design accomplished: %

■ Design before financial close   ■ Design before start of works on site

It should be realised that work done before financial close is in some sense work done 'at risk'. If financial close is not achieved, the costs of developing the design will have to be written-off, either by all the members of the SPV or by its principal designer. On the other hand, start of work on site is normally timetabled to follow so shortly after financial close that, if the design is not to be developed 'at risk', then some form of 'fast track' working, in which design and construction can run in parallel, will be required. Moreover, if design is mostly developed after financial close, innovations arising in the course of developing the design can make less contribution to the estimated cost savings incorporated into the bid price.

3.9 Participant organisations and their expertise

Size and experience of the participant organisations

The average size of the participant organisation teams in PFI projects is shown in Table 3.15. From the table it is evident that clients get large numbers of people involved in the PFI deals. Each of the client advisers' teams are very frequently constituted of 2 or 3 professionals with 1 or 2 support staff. Among SPVs, the norm is for relatively small organisations, averaging about 15 people.

It should be noted that the figures in Table 3.15 are expressed as 'full-time equivalent' numbers, at the peak of activity on the PFI project for that organisation.

The experience of the individuals within the participant organisations is shown in Table 3.16. Of interest is the contrast between the experience of the private sector participants and the client's teams. In particular, the client advisers seem to provide the most experience both in other PFI schemes and in projects of the same type. In addition, from Table 3.17, it is possible to affirm that client advisers seem to be the ones doing most in terms of the effort input into training their staff, while the clients do the least.

Type of organisation	Professional/management staff	Support staff
Clients	39	13
Client advisers	4	2
SPVs	11	4
SPV suppliers	19	16

Table 3.15 *Size of the organisations participating in the PFI project*

Type of organisation	Proportion of professional/management staff with at least some experience in other PFI schemes: %	Proportion of professional/management staff with at least some experience in projects of the same type: %
Clients	8	17
Client advisers	59	64
SPVs	37	61
SPV suppliers	34	33

Table 3.16 *Experience of the organisations participating in the PFI project*

Type of organisation	Proportion of cases in which the staff has been trained in PFI-related issues: %
Clients	12
Client advisers	59
SPVs	16
SPV suppliers	24

Table 3.17 *Training for PFI in the organisations participating in the PFI project*

At this point we should consider one of the recommendations of the Egan Report. The improvement of supervisory and management skills at all levels was considered to be a key aspect in order to produce a radical change leading to the achievement of the set targets. In this respect, it seems that the effort is not being led from the public sector, but from the private sector, which sees future opportunities for business in the PFI industry.

Cultural change caused by PFI

The degree of cultural change caused within the participant organisations and perceived by the different respondents is shown in Fig. 3.26. These data show that for two-thirds of the clients' and SPVs' respondents, the cultural change was large or radical. Meanwhile, for the client advisers and SPV suppliers, the figure is around one-quarter and one-half, respectively.

In other words, the principal actors in the PFI contract are precisely the ones who are subject to most cultural change. Meanwhile, the advisers, contractors and other suppliers perceive PFI as part of their portfolio of activities, but it does not necessarily mean a radical change in their way of carrying out their business.

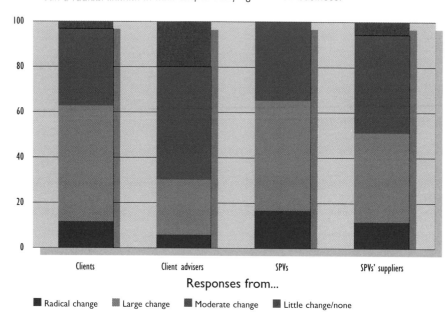

Figure 3.26 *Degree of cultural change experienced by the organisations participating in the PFI project*

Consider this point in combination with the fact that client advisers provide more PFI training for their own staff than anybody else. It might be inferred that advisory bodies, rather than the principal PFI organisations (clients and SPVs) are accumulating the knowledge and expertise on PFI. The question is then, how in the future can that knowledge be deployed in an effective and efficient way? Are important learning effects being produced in PFI organisations other than advisers?

Reasons for that cultural change

From Fig. 3.27, it is clear that working with new partners, and setting up new alliances have been the most difficult challenges for the clients' organisations.

In contrast, for the private sector, as shown in Fig. 3.28, the most important changes have been: 'bearing larger risks or risks formerly borne by other parties'; 'bearing much longer-term liabilities/commitments'; and 'being responsible for a widened scope of activities'. These relegate the problems of setting up new alliances and working with new partners to fourth or fifth place.

Again, this is an issue to be considered by policy makers within the public sector. There is clearly a need among public bodies for training on partnering arrangements and management of PFI contracts. However, it must be recognised that the diffuse but large teams deployed, presumably mostly part-time, by clients will be intrinsically harder to train than the smaller and more specialised teams deployed by advisers. Moreover, apart from a small number of centralised clients, it is unclear how training and experience gained by clients' staff will be effectively made available to future projects.

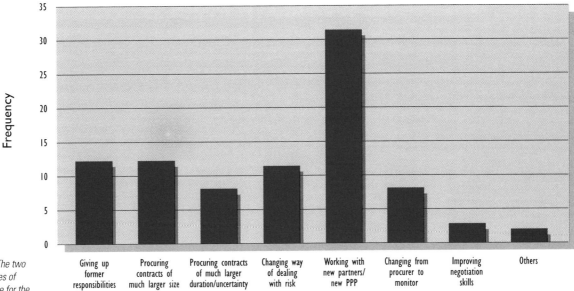

Figure 3.27 *The two principal causes of cultural change for the clients of the PFI project and their advisers*

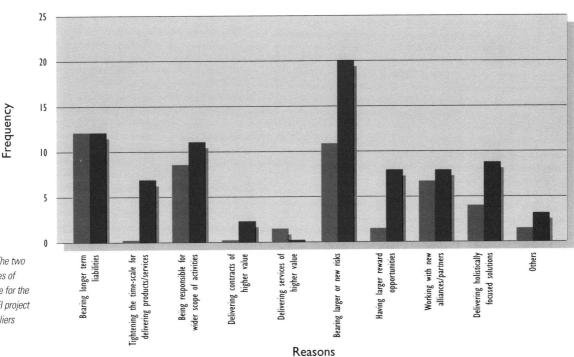

Figure 3.28 *The two principal causes of cultural change for the SPVs of the PFI project and their suppliers*

3.10 The form of the PFI VFM test

This section adds some descriptive aspects on the PFI procurement process carried out by the public sector clients. In particular, and relying on the TTF guidance, the enquiry asked how the public sector comparator (or other kind of value for money comparator – VFMC) was generated. The results of this enquiry are illustrated in Table 3.18. In only 13 out of 35 of the PFI projects sampled did clients use a VFMC in the form of a 'conventionally funded solution, providing a service of the same (similar) level as the one considered in the OS'.

However, when the same clients were asked for their opinion on what the comparator used represented, as shown in Fig. 3.29, they had very different opinions.

In fact, the sample of 30 clients was divided into three approximately equal parts: 'the option that might have offered the best VFM, if procured by the public sector'; 'the best VFM option within the existing affordability restraints'; and 'the only feasible alternative option for the public sector'. Who provided which of these three answers?

Type of comparator	Frequency
Conventionally funded solution, providing a similar level solution	13
Conventionally funded solution, providing a lower level solution ('do minimum', 'do nothing', 'do it later')	2
A PFI solution based on previous PFI projects	4
Others	16

Table 3.18 Types of comparator used by the clients of the PFI projects

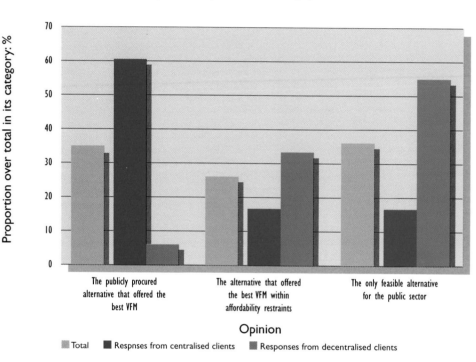

Figure 3.29 Clients' opinion about what the comparator of the PFI project represents

The details are shown in Fig. 3.29. Here, the respondents are grouped as centralised and decentralised clients. It is possible to say that there is a clear link between being a centralised public agency and the kind of alternative options available for generating the VFMC.

It seems clear from Fig. 3.29 that most decentralised clients are not able to compare PFI VFM with 'the best publicly procured alternative', and that the comparators used are heavily constrained by factors other than VFM. But equally it seems clear that centralised clients do undertake comparison of PFI VFM with 'the best publicly procured alternative', and that this is often judged to be the 'conventionally funded solution, providing a similar level of service'.

This may be fuelling the critics of the PFI process who doubt the real VFM that PFI represents for the provision of public services. Is the VFMC a 'best value' comparator and a plausible alternative option, as well? If not, the danger exists that the VFM test will come to be regarded by critics as just an exercise to justify the procurement of the necessary service through the only available source of funds, private investment.

In regard to the PSC, the research project also wanted to test whether a TTF guidance requirement (TTF Policy Statement No. 2, 1998), about the point in the process at which the PSC should be 'fundamentally' finished, was being observed. The TTF Policy Statement recommends that, for reasons of cost of preparation and of fairness to bidders, 'in general it is desirable to formalise the PSC as soon as possible'. The answers are illustrated in Fig. 3.30. We see that about 50% of the sample say that the VFMC was actually finished at the stage of OJEC publication (in effect, for the outline business case prior to approval to use PFI and invite bids). In another 38% of the cases the respondent declared work on the VFMC to have finished at or after BAFO (receipt of best and final offers) or the writing process of the final business case.

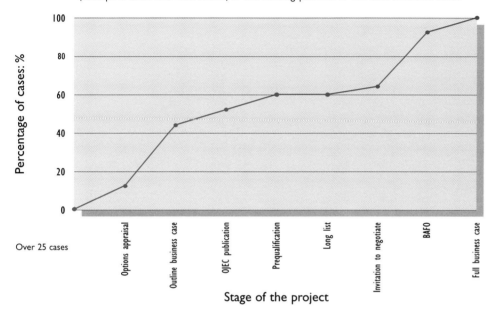

Figure 3.30 *Proportion of public sector comparators fundamentally finished by stage of the PFI project*

3.11 Future development of PFI

The results of the questions related to the future development of PFI give some idea of what the results of the PFI projects have been so far. Indeed, looking at the areas in which the respondents say they are working to make the PFI process more efficient/effective (Fig. 3.31), it is clear that PFI was still suffering teething problems, at the time of the survey.

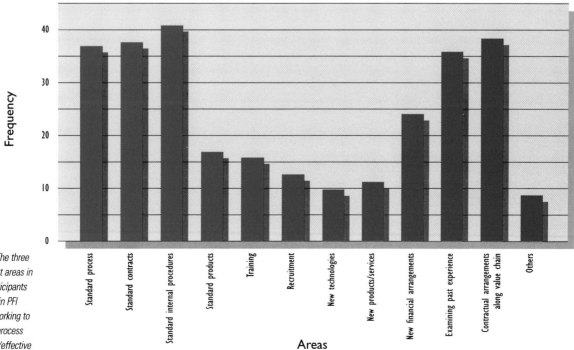

Figure 3.31 *The three most important areas in which the participants organisations in PFI projects are working to make the PFI process more efficient/effective*

The responses highlight, essentially, process aspects of PFI, rather than technical or learning ones. The actors are still concerned about how to get the deal done, rather than how to improve on it technically.

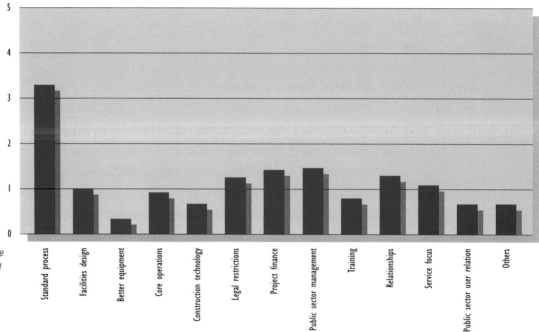

Figure 3.32 *Areas where CSIs might be generated in order to make the PFI process more efficient/ effective*

Looking at Fig. 3.32, areas where the potential for CSIs existed, the conclusion is similar. The participants consider that the potential for innovation lies in procedural aspects rather than technical aspects such as design, equipment, operation and construction.

It should then be necessary to study how these results evolve with new rounds of projects, or how more mature sectors differ from emerging ones.

Chapter 4

Factors affecting the extent of cost saving

Synopsis

On projects for centralised clients, reported total DBO cost savings had a median value of over 10%; whereas on projects for decentralised clients, median reported cost savings had a value estimated between 1% and 2%. The greater part of this significant difference arises from greater construction cost savings achieved in projects with centralised clients.

On building-based projects, reported total DBO cost savings had a median value of about 5%; whereas on civil engineering-based projects, median cost savings had a reported value estimated at about 12%. Again, the source of the difference almost certainly lies in greater construction cost savings achieved on civil engineering projects.

Custodial projects reported much higher total DBO cost savings than any other kind of building-based project.

Size of project does not appear to be significantly correlated with reported percentage DBO cost savings.

The scope of the PFI project (whether or not it includes provision of final services to users) is significantly correlated with reported percentage DBO cost savings (median of about 11% for 'complete service' projects, but of about 2–3% for 'partial service' projects).

The form of the OS (purely performance/functional or with a technical component) does not appear to be significantly correlated with reported percentage of DBO cost savings.

4.1   Introduction

Following on from the general results of Chapter 3, the key differences and similarities relating to the cost savings that have been achieved are shown in this section. The explanatory factors are taken both from the initial hypotheses of the investigation, and from the results obtained during the development of the research.

The research initially proposed that there would be a number of significant attributes of PFI that would affect the propensity to achieve CSIs and accrue cost savings (see Chapter 2). In this chapter we will explore a number of issues, detailed below.

- *Programme of projects versus one-off project.* This variable is associated with, but not the same as, the experience of the client procuring the project. It may also be associated with the level of expertise and experience that the private participants are contributing. The existence of a programme of projects should produce a different attitude among the private participants. They would be expected to have aspirations to obtain future work in the same tightly-focused market and, thus, they may be both more willing to invest in order to obtain learning benefits for the following rounds of projects, and be regarded by clients as less likely to behave opportunistically and 'hold up' the client after contract signature, when the fundamental transformation in the relative positions of client and contractor occurs. Clients in turn may accordingly be more prepared both to use 'incomplete contracts' (see Chapter 2, Section 2.5) and to commit their own transaction-specific investments. With those issues in mind, and as a simplified way of taking them into account, the projects have been classified into two groups: those with 'centralised clients' and those with 'decentralised clients'. The cost savings achieved by each of these groups are then analysed and the results commented upon in Section 4.2.

- *Type of facility.* In order to take into account the differences that the varied types of facility involved in the PFI procurement can make to the performance of the projects, it is necessary to group those projects in a convenient way for the analysis. Balancing the need for a detailed analysis and the statistical significance of the results considering the size of the sample, a simple division of projects is required. Furthermore, given the results of Chapter 3, in which civil engineering and building projects were shown to display different behaviour, a simple two-fold classification in these terms is justified as the basis for further investigation. This is presented in Section 4.3.

- *Size of the project.* This constitutes a factor commonly considered as an explanatory variable of the success of PFI. To analyse its effects, the sampled population has been divided into four quartiles, according to the level of capital investment involved in each case. The results of the analysis and conclusions are presented in Section 4.4.

- *Scope of the service provided.* One of the initial hypotheses of the research considered this as a determinant factor, and the analysis is pursued here. The classification of projects has been made according to the available information, between projects that comprise the provision of a fairly complete part of the core operations of the respective final service and those in which PFI includes only a part of those operational services. The latter usually include only FM, and ancillary services, excluding the associated core operations. The analysis is presented in Section 4.5.

- *Type and amount of prescriptive information provided.* Concern has been expressed that public sector clients may restrict the innovative behaviour of the bidders by providing excessively prescriptive information as to the solution required. This point was also taken into account in the analysis. Again, it was necessary to choose a simple way of grouping the available sample, in order to balance the needs for detail and statistical significance. To do so, the sample of responses was divided between those in which the informants declared that there was a preliminary design at the bidding stage and those in which there was not. It is argued that this is a good indicator of the amount of prescription provided by the client. Additionally, the kind of output specification (OS) supplied was considered. The kind of OS declared to be received by the SPV was analysed against the estimations of cost savings achieved. This analysis is presented in Section 4.6.

For each type of analysis indicated above, an analysis of variance of the reported cost savings distributions was carried out. First, this was made using all the seven intervals of reported cost savings used to collect the information in the questionnaire. Then, it was made using only four composite intervals. And finally, using only two broad intervals. For the last case, and only for the mathematical treatment and presentation, we defined reported cost saving over 5% as 'successful' and under 5% as 'unsuccessful'.

The statistical tool applied in each case is the well-known chi-squared test, and that is complemented by the graphical analysis. The combination of results allows the authors to draw the conclusions presented in this chapter. An example of the statistical tests applied is presented in Appendix A.7, in relation to the case described in Section 4.2 and illustrated in Fig. 4.1.

4.2 Programme of projects versus one-off project or centralised versus decentralised clients

The analysis of the variance in total cost savings by dividing the project sample into centralised and decentralised clients shows a clear difference in favour of the projects of centralised clients. This difference is statistically significant. While the median of the first distribution (centralised clients' projects) is located over 10% of savings relative to the correspondent benchmark or comparator, for the latter (decentralised clients' projects) the median is located slightly above zero savings (estimated at 1–2%). It is therefore possible to say that there is a statistically significant correlation between the fact of the client being centralised and the estimations of total cost savings in the project (see Fig. 4.1).

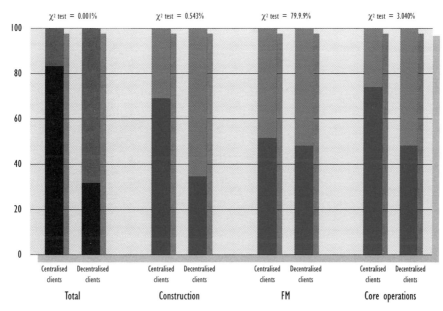

Figure 4.1 Programme of projects versus one-off project

It is possible to state tentatively that construction cost savings account for a non-negligible part of the greater total cost savings reported for centralised clients.

In the case of FM and core operation cost savings, there is no statistical significance in the differences of the distributions in favour of centralised clients. This means that it is impossible to say that the two groups behave differently with regard to the savings in operations.

We then turn to the category called 'other fees'. The results of the analysis show a picture of decentralised clients' projects being more seriously affected by this factor. However, the difference is not statistically significant. Decentralised clients' projects would be expected to face greater fees costs (legal advice, due diligence activities) in the PFI contract, on the basis of special due diligence issues (such as risks of financial default by the client or risk of the client acting outside their legal powers), lesser experience of clients and fewer opportunities to employ 'departmental model' contracts.

Therefore, it may be concluded that there is a clear relationship between the existence of a programme of projects, led by a centralised public sector organisation, and the chances of achieving total cost savings in each project. The sources of those savings certainly include savings achieved on construction costs. However, the tendencies that seem to exist in FM, core operations and procurement costs are not statistically significant. For more details on the data and the tests that support these statements, please refer to Appendix A.8.

4.3 Influence of the kind of facility involved – building versus civil engineering projects

To increase the number of observations in each category and to improve the opportunity to establish statistical significance, the analysis of the total cost savings by type of facility was carried out by classifying types of facility into building and civil engineering. We see that the building projects have been able to achieve less total cost savings than the civil engineering projects. However, the statistical significance of some of the results is not very high.

The median of the civil engineering projects' distribution of answers is located around 12% of savings over the benchmark or comparator, whereas for the building projects the median is located at about 5%. It is therefore possible to say that there is a definite correlation between the type of facility – building or civil engineering – and the estimations of total cost savings in the project (see Fig. 4.2).

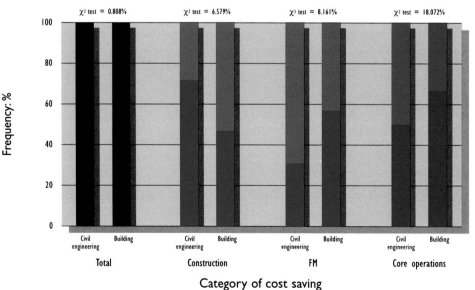

Figure 4.2 Building versus civil engineering projects

Separate analysis of the results for construction cost savings alone show a difference in the same direction. The statistical significance of this difference is low, but it would seem that a difference in construction cost savings accounts for a part of the difference in total cost savings.

Considering both kinds of operating cost together (FM and core operations) building projects show a higher median percentage of cost savings compared to civil engineering projects. In the former, a majority report savings of over 5%, while less than half of respondents do so for the latter.

In summary, it seems that the civil engineering projects achieve more cost savings than the building projects. The source of the differences on those savings lies, most probably, in the construction cost savings.

An additional analysis was carried out based on a complete classification by type of facility. From Fig. 4.3 it can be seen that the custodial sector is also a 'successful' one, despite falling within the building projects category. In fact, the three types of facility showing the largest savings are transport, utilities and custodial. Unfortunately, differences between individual types of facility cannot be analysed statistically because of the size of the sample. Ex post, grouping projects into 'civil engineering plus custodial sector' and 'building (non-custodial)', as in Fig. 4.4, produces highly statistically significant differences in reported cost savings.

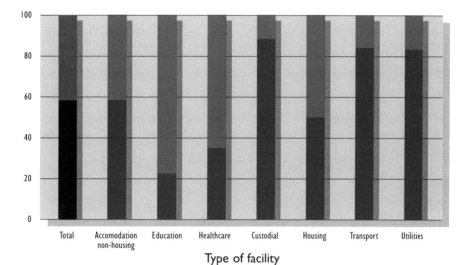

Figure 4.3 Total cost saving by type of facility

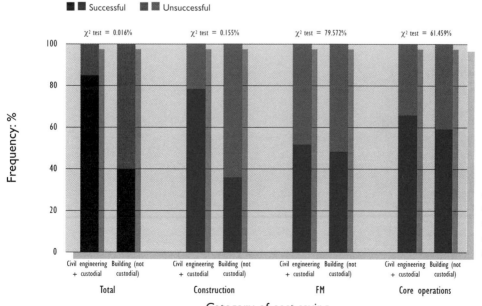

Figure 4.4 Civil engineering plus custodial sector versus building (non-custodial) projects

The data used to build Figure 4.4 (see Appendix A.8) show that while the median of the distribution of reported total savings is located around 12% for the 'civil engineering plus custodial' group, for the 'building (not custodial)' group the median is located around 2–3%. The great majority (over 80%) of respondents from the former group report 'success' (a total cost saving of over 5%), whereas only 40% of respondents for the latter group do so.

The difference in median results between these two groups is greatest (and statistically highly significant) for reported construction cost savings.

In the cases of FM and core operations cost savings, the regrouping achieved by reallocating custodial projects eliminates the previous difference in favour of 'building' projects.

In conclusion, it is possible to say that the division into civil engineering (transport and utilities) and building (all other) projects suggests that the former achieve more cost savings than the latter. However, the difference, considering the small size of the sample (of civil engineering projects, in particular), is not large enough to demonstrate this firmly. Nonetheless, when the classification is altered by adding the custodial sector to the civil engineering projects, those differences are very clearly demonstrated. In other words, the transport, utilities and custodial sectors seem to be the most successful in the achievement of total cost savings. The main reason for this is that they are consistently reporting more cost savings in construction than projects based on all the other types of facility. For more details, see Appendix A.8.

4.4 Size of the project

It is often asserted within the PFI industry that PFI projects have to be of a substantial size if they are to succeed in offering value for money. It is then interesting to explore how different the performance of the small projects has been in relation to the larger ones'. This section presents the analysis of cost savings by size of project.

The respondents in the sample each indicated the capital investment cost of the project to which their response referred. This was our preferred measure of size, to avoid complications arising from use of different discount rates in different projects to compute net present values of total costs, capital and operating costs.

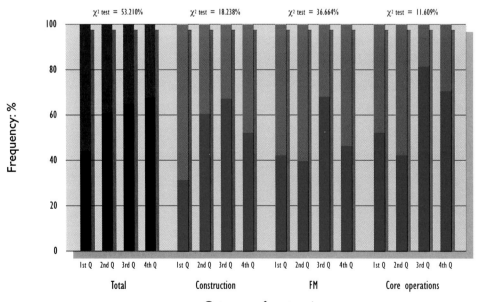

Figure 4.5 Cost savings by size of the projects (quartiles)

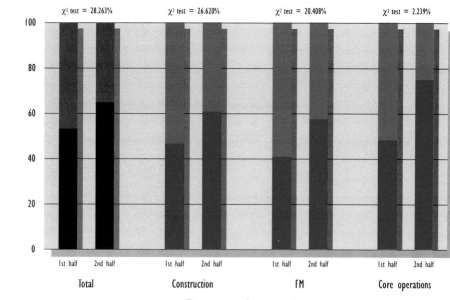

Figure 4.6 Cost savings by size of the projects (halves)

■ ■ Successful   ■ ■ Unsuccessful

Responses were arrayed by reported size of project and the size distribution of the set of responses was plotted. Responses were then divided into four quartiles and two halves according to their capital investment:

1st Q: £0–12m;   2nd Q: £13–42m;   3rd Q: £43–99m;   4th Q: £100m+;

while the 1st half comprises 1st plus 2nd quartiles; and 2nd half, 3rd plus 4th quartiles. The results, for both quartiles and halves of the size distribution, seem to cast doubt upon the general opinion mentioned above. Both in the cases of a quartile classification and the classification in halves, our findings are similar and are as shown in Figs 4.5 and 4.6. Graphically, there seems to be a certain tendency for the larger projects to obtain slightly more total cost savings. However, only one of the differences (core operation costs) is statistically significant with 10% confidence.

In other words, it is impossible to say, from the sample evidence, that the size of project has a significant influence on its probability of being 'successful' (reporting a cost saving of over 5%). For more details, see Appendix A.8.

4.5 Differences in provision of service or complete versus partial service provision

One of our original hypotheses was that the provision of a complete service within the PFI contract would favour the realisation of cost savings. To explore this, the estimations of cost savings are analysed against this factor. The projects were divided, according to the available information, into two groups: 'complete service included in the PFI contract' and 'partial service included in the PFI contract'. An example of the former is the case of DCMF prisons, in which the concessionaires are responsible for the complete provision of the core services – custodial services. An example of the latter is the case of PFI healthcare contracts, where the concessionaires are responsible only for the provision of ancillary services, such as catering, energy supply, cleaning, and others, and not for clinical services.

Comparison of the total cost savings reported for 'complete service' and for 'partial service' projects shows a clear and statistically significant difference in favour of the former (see Fig. 4.7). While the median of the distribution of the former is located at around 11% total cost savings, for the latter, the median is located slightly above zero savings (estimated at 2–3%).

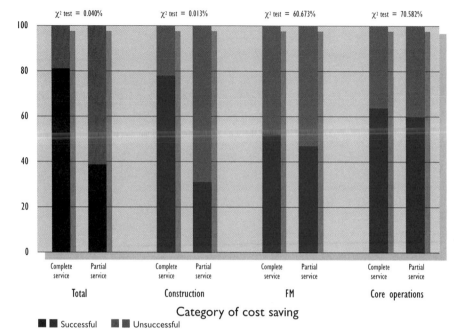

Figure 4.7 Cost saving by scope of the service provision within the PFI contract

The results of the analysis of the construction cost savings demonstrate the same tendency, with even more clarity than for total costs. It is then possible to state that the difference in construction cost savings accounts for a fairly important part of the difference in total cost savings reported for the two groups.

Graphically, there seems to be a tendency for complete service projects to report larger savings in FM costs. However, statistically it is not significant.

In the case of costs of core operations themselves, it is noteworthy that there is virtually no difference between the two groups in the median reported savings or in the proportion reporting savings of over 5%. Thus, for the partial service group, respondents appear to be reporting savings in costs of services falling outside the scope of the PFI contract that were of a similar order to the savings obtained by PFI when these core operations are part of the contract. If this interpretation of the findings is correct, then the significance of inclusion of core services lies not in any direct effect of inclusion on the cost of core services themselves, but rather in the indirect effects which inclusion may have on achievement of savings in construction cost. Independently of this, however, it seems that the use of PFI procurement has permitted cost savings in core operations regardless of whether those operations are included in the scope of the PFI agreement or not.

Before endorsing this interpretation too firmly, however, we need to note three caveats. First, in cases where the majority of core operations lay outside the PFI agreement, respondents may have been less familiar with the full evidence on which to base informed opinions on achievement of savings in this area. Private sector respondents would have no direct source of information of their own on savings achieved in this area by the public sector, although propositions that their solutions would permit such savings may have formed part of their bid. Likewise, our public sector respondents may have had less complete knowledge of savings in activities that formed no direct part of the PFI project for which they were responsible, and which were not elements in the public sector comparator or VFMC. Second, it is possible that some respondents on projects without a core operations element within the PFI agreement may have missed our guidance on how to interpret this part of the questionnaire, and classed some of the FM services that were part of the contract as 'core'. Finally, in some projects, while the majority of core operations may lie outside the scope of the PFI agreement (so that they are clearly not cases of 'complete service') nevertheless some such elements are included. For example, while most clinical services are clearly outside the scope of hospital PFI agreements, some medical or para-medical services may be included. It may be only these elements to which respondents in the 'partial service' category were referring in their answers on core operations costs.

It is therefore possible to conclude that there is a clear difference between the cost savings reported by complete and partial services projects. The probability of a project reporting total cost savings of over 5% is significantly greater if it is a complete service project. This factor has a significant influence on the level of total cost savings reported. The source of those savings is found mainly in the savings achieved on construction costs. For more details, see Appendix A.8.

4.6 Form of specification at the bidding stage and existence of preliminary design

The study also tackled the issue of the form of the specification and related information provided to the private participants in the PFI project. Two analyses were carried out. First, responses were grouped into those where the client provided a preliminary design of the facilities at the bidding stage and those where the client did not. Second, responses were classified according to the type or form of the OS.

Graphically, there seems to be a tendency for the cases with provision of preliminary designs to achieve higher total cost savings (see Fig. 4.8). However, the statistical significance is negligible. The same comments (graphical inspection showing some positive difference but not statistically significant) apply in the case of construction cost savings.

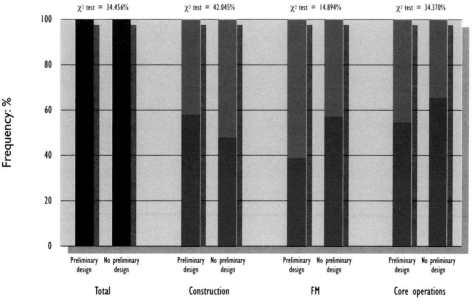

Figure 4.8 Cost savings by provision of preliminary design of facilities at bidding stage

For FM and core operations, graphical inspection seems to show a negative relationship of preliminary design with cost savings. This relationship is of no statistical significance, however. In summary, it is possible (but not statistically confirmed) that the provision of preliminary designs supports the achievement of total cost savings, through the reduction in construction costs. This just outweighs a clearer but apparently in aggregate no larger effect in the opposite direction upon the achievement of operation savings. This suggests that, in estimating total costs, and thus total cost savings for these projects, our respondents gave a lower 'weight' to FM costs than to construction costs.

It will be recalled (Chapter 3) that our respondents were quite firmly of the opinion that the form of the OS (performance, functional or technical) was an important factor influencing the opportunity to make CSIs and thus to achieve VFM. However, analysis of this factor against reported cost savings did not yield statistical confirmation of that relationship.

Graphical inspection of Figs 4.9 and 4.10 seems to suggest some unexpected relationships between the different types of output specification and differences in the extent to which cost savings are achieved.

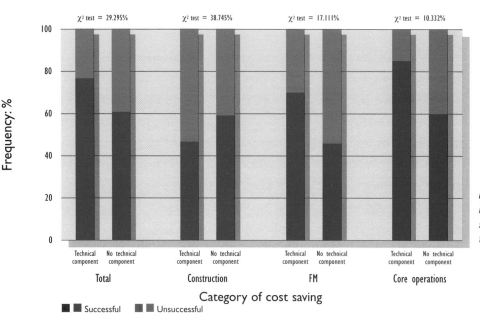

Figure 4.9 Cost savings by use of output specifications with technical components

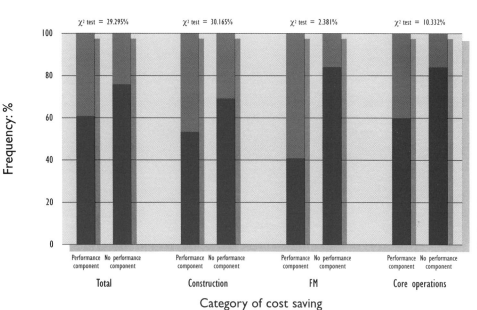

Figure 4.10 Cost savings by use of output specifications with performance components

Grouping projects into those for which the OS had no technical component and those which did have such a component (the latter being a small number and small proportion of the sample; 13 out of 62 useable responses to this question) shows (Fig. 4.9) a higher proportion of the latter to have been 'successful' (reported total cost savings of over 5%). This difference appears to arise from greater success in saving operating costs. This result is against expectations, which were that a technical (in this context, architectural or engineering design) specification would have a particularly constraining effect on the search for innovations to save 'whole life' (operating) costs.

Graphical comparison (Fig. 4.10) of cost savings in projects with and without a performance component in the OS likewise showed an unexpected result, with success in achieving total and construction cost savings more frequent in projects without a performance component in their specification. For operating cost savings, the direction of the expected relationship was ambiguous, because in this context absence of a performance OS may be taken to imply less risk to the provider that failure to achieve a given level of operating service provision will be penalised, and thus a more favourable trade-off between benefits (expected cost savings) and risks (loss of revenues if the innovation endangers service delivery standards) from CSIs. The argument depends on there being a positive relationship between the use of performance elements in the OS and the number of separate service performance targets in the payment mechanism. The greater the number of separate service performance targets to which payment is linked, the stronger this effect might be.

However these differences do not pass the test for statistical significance. The nearest approach to significance is for FM costs in relation to a performance component of the OS (success in achieving FM cost savings is twice as likely if the OS does not contain a performance component). Further investigation would be required to resolve this relationship. It is possible that some participants find it too difficult to interpret unfamiliar performance specifications, or that this mode of specification encourages greater 'caution' in providers, since payment is linked to measured performance, or that a larger sample would show no such relationship.

Summing up, the evidence collected for this research does not clearly support or refute the proposition that the provision of any particular kind of OS increases the opportunities of achieving cost savings. For more details, see Appendix A.8.

Chapter 5

Sectoral studies

Synopsis

In this chapter, the three most important (by value and number of PFI projects to date) sectors of the PFI market are each discussed holistically. The aim is to gain some insight into how explanatory factors affecting CSI either combine with and reinforce one another, or counteract and neutralise one another.

In the case of the custodial sector, the following combination of factors seems to have created positive synergies of outcome:

(a) a traditional procurement and provision process seen as relatively and absolutely inefficient

(b) a complete service scope to the PFI contracts

(c) a highly centralised client (HM Prison Service), obtaining advantages both from experience gained on earlier projects and from possession of a future programme of projects

(d) a small but sufficient number of increasingly experienced private sector competitors

(e) scope for quite distinct innovation strategies to yield similar levels of cost saving.

In the case of the highways sector, the following combination of factors seems to have created positive synergies of outcome:

(a) a traditional procurement and provision process generally perceived as quite efficient, but with clear scope for gains from technologically-based innovation by integrating responsibility for operation with responsibility for design and construction

(b) a highly centralised and increasingly experienced client (Highways Agency), which has already learned enough from its PFI experience to change significantly its initial payment-and-risk structure (based on shadow tolls) to a new structure based on lane availability; and which has, to an unequalled degree, deliberately experimented with different contents of PFI projects so as to learn for itself which types of project work best as PFIs

(c) a small but sufficient number of increasingly experienced private sector consortia focused on this sector, and with very substantial pre-PFI experience in highways design, construction and maintenance

(d) preliminary designs and output specifications (OS) which, although containing a technical and therefore potentially prescriptive element, have in fact (in combination with appropriate operating cost risk transfer) allowed private sector providers to focus on the potential economies of integrating operation into design and construction (see (a) above) which happened to be considerable in this case.

In the case of the healthcare sector, the following combination of factors seems largely to have neutralised or offset whatever positive 'enablers' of innovation were present:

(a) procurement clients (hospital trusts) that were also to be the actual users of the services provided in the PFI contracts

(b) decentralised clients, each likely only to procure one PFI project for the foreseeable future

(c) clients facing a relatively high level of uncertainty concerning their requirements

(d) apparently, limited technological scope for major CSIs.

On the other hand, the scope in the healthcare sector for PFI to deliver an improved standard of facility management and ancillary service provision appears to be greater than the scope to deliver CSIs.

5.1 Analysis of three sectors

Following the previous more general analysis, three particular sectors are now examined. These are the healthcare sector, the custodial sector and the highways sector. The results from the survey have been augmented where necessary by a more detailed exploration of the issues facing these sectors by means of interviews. The value of this is that it illustrates the issues present in these sectors, without becoming excessively biased to one particular viewpoint.

These three sectors together represent 45% of the total number of projects addressed in the survey, and represent 32% of the total capital costs of the sample. (If PRIME, which represents 41% of the total capital costs of the sample, is taken out, the three chosen sectors account for 54% of the total value of the remaining projects.)

The three sectors cover both poles of the range of reported success in achieving cost saving – roads and prisons represent the most successful types of project, and hospitals represent one of the least successful.

At the same time, these three sectors cover the following ranges of explanatory variables. Highways and custodial sectors have centralised clients, while the healthcare sector is the opposite. Roads are civil engineering projects, while the other two are building projects. In the case of roads, projects are of medium to large size; in the case of healthcare, a group of small size projects and another group of medium–large size exist; and in the case of prisons, all projects are of small to medium size in terms of capital investment. The custodial and the highways sectors include core operation services in the PFI contract, while the healthcare projects only include ancillary services. The custodial sector uses very flexible OS, while the healthcare sector seems to include fairly prescriptive preliminary designs, due to the existence of interfaces between the operations included in the PFI contract and those excluded from it. In the case of road projects, very complete preliminary designs are enclosed in the tendering documentation, but they are considered as reference points for the designs to be developed by the bidders. These characterisations are illustrated in Table 5.1.

In summary, these three sectors are considered to be sufficiently representative to be worthy of a focused review. This is both because they represent a large part of the PFI industry, present and future, and because they are characterised by different key variables that seem to explain, to a large extent, the cost saving and innovation behaviour of PFI.

Characteristic	Healthcare sector	Custodial sector	Highways sector
Programme of projects versus one-off project	Decentralised clients	Centralised clients	Centralised client
Type of facility	Building	Building	Civil engineering
Size of project	Small projects and medium to large projects	Small to medium projects	Medium to large
Scope of service provided	Ancillary services	Core services	Core services
Type and amount of information at tendering	Performance – functional type of OS Compulsory preliminary designs included in most cases	Performance – functional type of OS No preliminary designs at all	Performance – technical type OS Proposal of preliminary designs included

Table 5.1 *Summary of three-sector characteristics*

5.2. Healthcare sector

The following text is taken from NAO Report on Dartford & Gravesham Hospital (p.18):

"The NHS Executive now require that Regional Offices (which succeeded Regional Health Authorities in 1996) and key purchasers of health services such as Health Authorities should take a greater role in the planning of new hospitals. They have also introduced the NHS Capital Prioritisation Advisory Group to assess all major schemes to ensure that they are consistent with the local health strategy and advise Ministers on their relative health service need. In taking forward this work, the NHS Executive might also consider whether there are opportunities for savings through awarding more than one project to a particular consortium. The existence of these opportunities may depend upon factors such as geographical proximity, synergy in the composition of hospital projects and parallel running of procurements.

The NHS Executive also now require that a funding ceiling be set for each project and this should be clearly defined and agreed by the NHS Trust and the Health Authority taking account of all the costs associated with the project. The NHS Executive have emphasised that the robustness of the affordability calculations and the assumptions behind them should be thoroughly vetted at an early stage and kept under review throughout the procurement process.

Since the launch of the PFI, the NHS Executive have sought to exploit the benefits of collaboration with the private sector and in particular the opportunities offered from this source of finance to provide new or improved hospital facilities. Against a background of competing demands on public sector funding for capital schemes, Trusts were required to assess the potential for using PFI for all new hospital developments and refurbishments. The NHS Executive also stipulated that they demonstrate value for money on each project, Trusts should compare the costs and benefits of the PFI option against costs of traditional procurement – the Public Sector Comparator. These requirements were embodied in the Guidance on PFI projects issued by the NHS Executive in March 1995. This guidance built on the Executive's earlier guidance of 1994 on appraising and managing NHS capital projects.

There were many instances of long standing projects that could not be funded adequately because of the lack of public capital, the need for backlog maintenance and the demands of existing contractual commitments."

The earlier, but still relatively recent, reorganisation of the NHS hospital-based services into separate purchasers (Health Authorities) and providers (NHS Trusts) had set the fundamental context within which healthcare PFI projects were situated. A decade or so earlier, the healthcare sector would have been a much more centralised (specifically, a centralised/regionalised rather than localised) client for PFI. PFI would then have fitted into a national/regional programme of procurement of new hospital facilities and related ancillary services. Instead, a set of local entities established to manage the provision of clinical services, the NHS Trusts, became the purchasers of ancillary services from PFI companies.

The Trusts were, as a result of this restructuring, able in theory to integrate procurement of facilities and ancillary services with provision of clinical services, thus overcoming a separation between Regional Authorities acting as clients for new hospital construction projects and the bodies that would be responsible for operating those hospitals and using them to provide clinical services. However, this gain in potential integration has to be set against problems created on three fronts: inability to develop a programme of PFI projects, and to benefit directly from experience gained in early projects; problems of 'affordability' created by the limited and uncertain level of Trust income; and problems of capital budgeting, associated with absence of any central prioritising and ranking of what were, in effect, competing 'bids' from different local Trusts for the scarce resources available to pay for new hospitals.

As a direct result of the last problem, some PFI proposals were developed by Trusts, and put out to PFI tender, which offered poor returns in terms of benefit-to-cost ratios when compared with other capital schemes within the hospital sector, or which did not meet nationally-identified 'priority needs'. Eventually, most of these proposed PFI schemes were cancelled, but not before much abortive expenditure of time, effort and money.

For a project to offer good value for money to the NHS it is not merely necessary to demonstrate that PFI offers the most cost effective way of providing that particular project, but also, and more fundamentally, that any version of that project offers better social returns on investment than its opportunity cost, in terms of other projects foregone because of its claim on scarce funds. Avoidance of a direct public sector capital expenditure budget or borrowing constraint, by using PFI, in no way removes the scarcity of public sector resources from which the costs of all competing projects, capital or current, must eventually be met.

PFI contracts are normally fixed for periods of 25 years or more. The terms of the purchaser/provider contracts for clinical services between Health Authorities and Trusts, in contrast, are fixed for much shorter periods. Thus, on the one hand, the Trust has to commit itself to a long-term statement of its requirements in terms of serviced facilities, when these requirements are in fact derived from its uncertain future agreements to provide clinical services to the Health Authority; and, on the other hand, the PFI company has to consider and deal with the risks arising from the uncertain size of the Trust's future revenues.

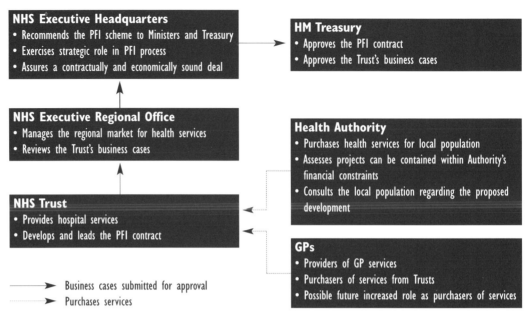

Figure 5.1 *Relationship of bodies involved in the letting of the PFI Healthcare Contract*

In terms of the conceptual model set out in Chapter 2, PFI in the healthcare sector is the locus of major uncertainty and low transaction frequency (repetition). This, we would predict, would raise the relative transaction costs of PFI, compared with some other forms of procurement. We would expect this to 'show up' in relatively high levels of fees, and in greater difficulty in finding appropriate briefs and specifications.

We would expect the exclusion of final (clinical) services from the scope of PFI in this sector to generate a problem. By constraining the scope for the PFI company to rethink the whole hospital healthcare provision process and removing its ability to benefit from cost savings in core operations, it limits both its incentive and its capability to make cost-saving innovations. We would also expect the short-term contracts existing between NHS trusts and health authorities to generate another problem. By creating a need to describe and specify requirements for ancillary services under a range of possible conditions of requirement for final services, it greatly increases the difficulty of forming an appropriate PFI contract.

Figure 5.1, adapted from the NAO Report on the Dartford and Gravesham Hospital (NAO,1999), shows the organisation of the public bodies involved in letting a PFI hospital contract.

On the issue of inclusion of clinical services in the scope of PFI contracts, we accept the point made to us by the NHS Executive that, as well as accountability issues, there are powerful economic arguments against this, including:

• the difficulty of then designing contracts which avoid giving incentives to the supplier to 'induce' demand.

• the need to avoid the danger of PFI clinical providers 'poaching' scarce clinical resources from other NHS hospitals.

PFI healthcare sector versus traditional provision: scope for rethinking the process

According to the respondents to the survey, the greatest scope for rethinking the process within traditionally procured healthcare projects is found in the briefing, design and procurement processes. The results of the survey show a set of similar scores for the healthcare sector in all the categories to those for the total sample (see Table 5.2).

Type of facility	Brief	Design	Construction	Operations	Third party revenue	Procurement
Total sample	3.6	3.5	3.3	3.5	2.6	3.8
Healthcare	3.9	3.8	3.4	3.5	2.6	3.7
Custodial	4.5	3.6	3.5	4.4	2.5	4.0
Roads	2.6	3.8	3.6	2.9	1.5	3.9

Table 5.2 *Average relevance of scope for CSIs in traditionally procured projects of three sectors*

Moreover, considered specifically as individual projects, the healthcare sector shows a balance of scope for innovation between the construction and the operations-related aspects. The peaks are achieved in quality management, improving the durability of assets and the procurement structure (see Table 5.3).

Type of facility	Excess capacity	Excess durability	Excess of risk protection	Construction speed	Buildability	Standard components	Quality Management	Improving asset durability	Space planning	Operation staff	Other operations	Mix new building and refurbishment	Non-functional elements elimination	New technologies (construction and operation)	Procurement	Other
Total sample	2.6	2.4	3.2	3.1	3.4	3.1	3.5	3.3	3.1	3.4	3.0	2.1	2.9	3.3	3.6	0.8
Healthcare	2.9	2.5	3.1	3.2	3.3	3.1	3.5	3.6	3.4	3.4	3.2	2.3	2.9	3.1	3.5	0.5
Custodial	3.2	3.3	3.7	3.6	3.8	3.7	3.9	3.5	4.4	4.2	3.6	1.6	3.4	3.7	3.9	0.6
Roads	1.5	2.6	4.1	3.5	4.4	3.1	4.0	3.4	1.3	3.6	2.0	2.2	2.1	3.6	3.7	1.2

Table 5.3 *Average relevance of scope for CSIs in the PFI projects of three sectors*

In other words, it is the respondents' view that the method of procuring and designing hospitals needed to be updated before PFI; and that in actual PFI projects as they have arisen, construction quality management and designing for greater durability have allowed most opportunities for CSIs.

Savings achieved in PFI healthcare projects

From the analysis of cost savings reported in the healthcare sector, it is not possible to affirm that the PFI projects have been successful. Assessing the savings relatively, the largest are shown in the area of facilities management, while certain modest savings are identified in terms of construction costs. In contrast, large additional costs are reported in fees. The overall result is that the total savings are very poor (see Fig. A.3 in Appendix A.6). It should be added that our evidence does not show that cost savings are better on the most recent projects.

Interestingly, some savings on core operations costs are reported, despite the fact that most PFI contracts for this kind of project do not include the majority of core services. Considering the way in which the question was phrased, this result has been interpreted as relating to those services included in the PFI contract that go beyond the FM of the premises. For example, catering, an element usually included in such contracts, might be the matter of the reported savings.

However, the scope and extent of the savings achieved in the clinical services kept in the hands of the NHS Trusts are not clear from this study. This will be addressed in the respective business cases and is currently a matter of discussion in the industry. Is it the case that the method of provision of core services outside the PFI contract might be optimised thanks to the existence of the PFI contract? On this point, see the Queen Elizabeth II Hospital case study in Chapter 6. This might happen in order to make the PFI contract viable. Some NHS Trusts may have to go through a re-engineering exercise of their own operation processes, in order to detach the elements to be included in the PFI contract. But again, it is possible that such an exercise would be stimulated by any procurement of a new hospital.

This discussion seems to be consistent with other studies in the area of PFI healthcare projects (NAO, 1999; Unison, 1999). These put a question mark on the actual results achieved in this kind of project. However, in interviews with other sources in the public and private sector sides of the PFI healthcare sector we found that our informants remained positive about the achievement in healthcare PFIs to date, and consider these projects as innovative, necessary, and efficient and estimate that this type of project would not be procured with such quality and reliability, out of the PFI environment. The positive emphasis of our informants was not on cost savings achieved, which they explicitly or tacitly recognised had been disappointing, but on the superior quality of service and of facility found in the PFI projects.

Sources of innovation in PFI healthcare projects

As in any other sector, the most common innovations in the healthcare sector are incremental. In addition, some prototype solutions or adaptations from other industries seem to be implemented, while very few adaptations from overseas are reported. In this respect, this sector appears as typical of the building project type of PFI.

We had considered that the inclusion in some hospital PFI consortia of FM operators with experience in managing hospital facilities in other countries might have been important. However, it appears that either no set of superior practices exists in hospital FM outside the UK, or that the organisations involved are not structured so as to promote the transfer of such ideas.

A majority of the implemented innovations have no technological roots. In other words, the changes being implemented are fundamentally process-based rather than technology-based.

On the minority of innovations that are 'technological', the following comments apply. The areas of construction technology that appear to be more important than others are related to construction engineering, such as standardisation and prefabrication, and to communications/IT applications to construction. With regard to the areas of operations technology, the use of new equipment to replace employees is reported as the most important. However, it should be noted that only 60% of all healthcare sector respondents indicated any particular areas of technical innovation.

Among the reasons why the innovations that have occurred were not applied prior to the PFI project, only 40% of the healthcare sector respondents consider that non-existence of the necessary experience is a relevant point. This means that in their view the expertise, in general, existed but was not being used in the traditionally procured healthcare projects for other reasons (see Fig 5.2).

More than 60% of respondents in healthcare reported that organisational restrictions were relevant (see Fig. 5.3). It is also indicated that before the use of PFI, there was a lack of incentives to innovate. It seems that a PFI contractual environment (of incentive-based, partially integrated and long-term contracts) has supported the kinds of innovations implemented in the PFI healthcare sector. However, there are no clear benefits of that innovation in terms of cost savings.

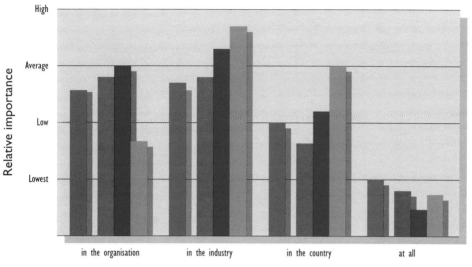

Figure 5.2 *Lack of available expertise as a reason why the CSIs generated in the PFI project were not previously implemented*

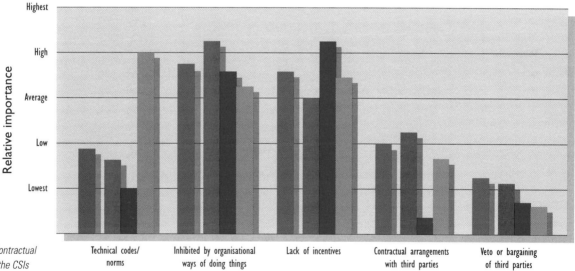

Figure 5.3 *Contractual reasons why the CSIs generated in the PFI project were not previously implemented*

In respect of providing a starting point for the bidders to generate innovation, in the majority of the healthcare cases bidders received fundamentally performance-functional OS, but with a previously developed design. The SPVs then added certain elements to those specifications, making them more technical, before transferring them to their suppliers.

The principal difficulty that the clients and their advisers report at the time of producing those OS is their lack of previous experience in PFI or projects of that type. Also reported, although to a lesser extent, are difficulties concerning the interfaces between existing and new facilities. The latter point is a typical problem in the health sector, as it might be also in education, where the core operations of existing facilities have to keep running while the new PFI services are provided. This problem is examined in the context of the Queen Elizabeth II Hospital case study in Chapter 6.

We asked the NHS Executive to comment on our findings. The following is our summary of the points they made.

• There continues to be progress in learning from the experience of the 'first wave' of NHS PFI schemes. In particular, there is now much greater central guidance and support, as well as the NHS PFI standard contract.

• There are measures in place designed to help each trust benefit from the experiences of others, both forums for trusts to network, and a programme (ProCure 21) of accreditation and training for project directors.

• There are plans for further standardisation of payment mechanisms and output specifications.

• A system for post-project evaluation is in place which will, in time, provide feedback on project attributes associated with success in achieving cost savings and VFM.

• For all NHS projects a PSC is required, and the form of this PSC is not allowed to be constrained by the availability of public sector capital finance.

We fully accept that the NHS Executive has been very active in developing measures designed to improve VFM outcomes on NHS PFI projects. Our point, however, is that its Private Finance Unit has to operate in a less favourable set of circumstances in this respect than is the case for HMPS or the Highways Agency.

5.3 Custodial sector

Since the early days of the Private Finance Initiative, HM Prison Service has been driving a programme of private investment in their capital projects. Before the launch of the PFI, the Prison Service had already begun to place private sector contracts for the management and operation of existing prisons. The Home Secretary announced, in the autumn of 1993, a further involvement of the private sector in the Prison Service. This was to take the form of invitations to design, construct, manage and finance (DCMF) six new prisons. The first two contracts, for prisons located at Fazakerley and Bridgend, were awarded in December 1995 and January 1996, respectively. Since then, a total of four rounds of DCMF prison projects have been completed.

One principal need of HM Prison Service has been to expand the capacity of its stock of prisons in terms of the number of prisoner places. Another has been to rethink the management of its prisons, both new and existing, so as to produce regimes more acceptable to HM Inspector of Prisons and to achieve efficiency gains. Importantly, overcrowding in prisons was becoming an increasingly serious cause for concern. Public funds were made available to pay for a prison building programme. PFI was seen by the Prison Service management as a way forward for the provision of public services in the sector which would combine both its objectives – provision of the maximum number of new prisoner places in the near future, and 'experimental' introduction of new ways of providing new prisoner regimes. It seems clear to us from our interviews and other sources that the Prison Service anticipated possible resistance to 'regime' changes from the established Prison Officers' Association and from its members, and considered that these changes might be introduced more readily, and more cheaply, in DCMF prisons. The Home Office would act as an enabler, benefiting from appropriate private sector skills in the provision of the custodial services. This was expected to improve the value for money of these projects.

According to an earlier NAO Report (NAO, 1994) in 1994, the Prison Service estate comprised 131 prisons of varying types, size and age. There were 48 pre-First World War establishments, dating mostly from the 19th century; 30 service camps and 9 country house establishments, taken over for prison use after the Second World War; and 44 purpose built post-war establishments, including one under construction. No new prisons were built between 1918 and 1958. Thus, between 1958 and 1994 completion of purpose-built new prisons had averaged just over one per year (44 in 36 years), although this rate had accelerated towards the end of that period.

Despite significant fluctuations over time, due to changes in sentencing policy and measures taken to divert offenders from custody, the prison population had risen from 44 000 in 1982 to an expected 50 000 in 1995. This meant that overcrowding and a shortage of capacity of between 5000 to 7000 places was a typical feature in the 1980s and early 1990s, with projections of increasing pressure for additional places.

HM Prison Service began a major programme of building new prisons and improving existing ones in 1980, with the following objectives:

- to ease overcrowding
- to improve health, hygiene and safety to meet statutory requirements
- to provide access to night sanitation
- to improve physical security.

Between 1985 and 1994, 21 new prisons were opened (an average of two per year) and the annual capital expenditure rose 175% in real terms between 1987/88 and 1994 (from £115m to £315m, at constant 1993 prices).

The DCMF prison construction programme therefore constituted a natural continuation of the investment programme being implemented since the early 1980s. The inclusion of the PFI was considered as a means of improving the performance of the Prison Service in the procurement of such an ambitious investment plan.

PFI custodial sector versus traditional provision: scope for rethinking the process

The greatest scope for rethinking the process within traditionally procured custodial sector projects is found in the briefing and the operations processes. Although the results of the survey show a high score for the custodial sector in all the categories, the peaks are achieved in these two areas in particular. In third place, the procurement arrangements appeared as an important area of potential development in these projects (see Table 5.2).

The results obtained for the scope of innovation given by the PFI projects in the forms in which they had actually arisen, demonstrate that the custodial sector shows consistently the highest scores in most of the 16 categories presented. The highest scores are achieved in space planing and improving efficiencies of operation staff. There are also high scores for quality management, buildability, procurement and use of new technologies for construction and operations (see Table 5.3).

Therefore the traditional provision process was seen to suffer from significant inefficiencies in its briefing and operations processes. Similarly, procurement was also capable of improvement. These aspects were taken on board within PFI. In particular, it allowed rethinking of the briefing process, and therefore, the operating regimes, fostering the generation of new and innovative designs. Finally, private sector involvement and the freedom given to the SPVs has permitted them to pursue short construction periods, with an important emphasis on buildability, construction speed, elimination of excess of risk protection, use of standard components and quality management.

It is not without historical precedent that the emergence of a large and continuing construction programme led, in the Prison Service, to the strengthening of the competencies and also the power (vis-à-vis 'user' departments) of a centralised procurement function, close to top management of the Prison Service. This seems to have reduced the control formerly exercised by user departments over the formation of project briefs and approval of proposals. We attribute some, perhaps many, of the cost savings achieved to this organisational change. What cannot be known with any certainty, however, is the extent to which this restructuring within the Prison Service could have occurred to the same degree, and had similar results, without the involvement of PFI.

Savings achieved in the PFI custodial sector

The analysis of cost savings reported for the custodial sector shows a general success in all the categories, except in 'other fees' (see Fig. A.4 in Appendix A.6). The latter also appears as the only category with a high variance of answers. This would suggest that there is generally a clear agreement that cost savings have been achieved. Moreover, in 'other fees', the first projects show high increases in costs while the most recent projects show much lesser increases, if any. In other words, the extra costs due to legal fees, due diligence and others, have been overcome, or at least are under control, and no longer a source of significant uncertainty.

In terms of the other stages of the PFI project, the construction costs seem to be reduced substantially (the median locates between 10 and 15%) and a similar situation is found in respect of core operation costs, although the savings in FM seem to be smaller. These factors have allowed the PFI custodial sector to obtain median total cost savings between 10 and 15%, according to the indicators obtained in this research. These estimations are consistent with other publications, including the NAO reports. The additional value of this report is in the search for the explanatory factors behind those figures, when compared to other sectors.

Sources of innovation in the PFI custodial sector

As in all sectors, the most common innovations in the custodial sector are of an incremental nature. The difference, in respect of the average and other sectors, is the greater importance that prototype solutions acquire. At the same time, no significant number of adaptations from other industries seems to exist, while only in some cases do adaptations from other countries appear to be considered relevant. Therefore there is evidence to support the idea that this sector has carried out more radical innovation than others. Despite involvement of operators with experience abroad, it seems that importing innovations from other countries is not the norm.

There are similar proportions of technologically-rooted and non-technologically rooted innovations implemented in this case, but the evidence shows high variance in this proportion between projects, indicating a broad difference of strategy between some of the three PFI companies which dominate this sector.

In the area of construction technology, the most important aspects are those of standardisation and prefabrication. The majority of the respondents agree on this. In the area of operations technology, the use of new equipment to replace staff and new monitoring techniques appear to be the key aspects. However, only 50% of the total of custodial sector respondents indicated any particular aspects of operating technology.

Among the reasons why the implemented innovations were not applied before the PFI project, the non-existence of the necessary experience within the respective organisation or industry appears to be an important explanatory factor (see Fig. 5.2). This suggests that most of the PFI industry had to look for these solutions somewhere else, or simply create them. However, only around 60% of respondents in the custodial sector indicated any 'experience' factor as a reason.

It is also suggested that before the project, there was a lack of incentives to innovate or that organisational ways of doing things hindered the initiatives (see Fig. 5.3). Nearly 90% of custodial sector respondents indicated some such factor and there was a high level of agreement around the answers. It is possible then to conclude that a changed contractual environment has supported the kinds of CSI implemented in the PFI custodial sector. It has, in this case, allowed the generation of more radical innovation.

As the starting point for the bidders from which to generate such innovation, they received fundamentally performance-functional OS, with no previous design. The SPVs, on the other hand, added certain elements to those specifications, maybe even a preliminary design, but kept the performance-functional nature of the original OS, when transferring the brief to their suppliers.

5.4 Highways sector

The following text is taken from the NAO Report (The Private Finance Initiative: the first four design, build, finance and operate road contracts, 1998). Fig. 5.4, adapted from NAO (1998), sets out the relationships of the parties involved.

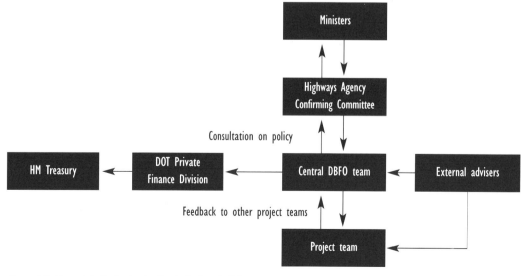

Figure 5.4 *Chart of the bodies involved in the letting of a PFI road project*

"The application of the Private Finance Initiative to road programmes was set out in two consultation documents – the Department of Transport's Green Paper Paying for better motorways (1993) and Design, Build, Finance and Operate Concessions for Trunk Roads and Motorways (1994). Under the proposals, the private sector would contract to build and operate a road for a period of 30 years. In return the Department would pay the private sector builder/operator according to the use made of the road. The mechanism they chose was known as 'shadow tolls': payments based on the number of vehicle kilometres travelled by road users. Road users would not pay directly for using the roads. Initial policy development and formulation of the Design, Build, Finance, and Operate contract terms was led by the Central Transport Group of the Department of Transport. Further development of the policy and procedures became a shared responsibility following the establishment of the Highways Agency in 1994. Implementation of the projects was carried out by the Highways Agency. The Agency established a Confirming Committee of the Agency Management Board which played a central role in steering the process through the negotiations. This board level involvement also demonstrated the Agency's commitment to the Design, Build, Finance, and Operate approach to all parties."

[Authors' note: subsequently the Highways Agency considered and introduced alternative payment mechanisms, based mainly on availability of lanes, instead of shadow tolls. NAO (1998) reported only on projects from Tranche 1 which, like Tranche 2, used shadow tolls.]

"Objectives defined by the Highways Agency for project Tranches 1 and 2 were:

- *maximise VFM by allocating risks appropriately*
- *ensure safe and satisfactory design, construction and operation of new and existing roads*
- *promote innovation*
- *test the enthusiasm of the market for DBFO road contracts (first tranche)*
- *assist in the establishment of a road operating industry within the private sector."*

PFI roads versus traditional provision: scope for rethinking the process

The greatest scope for rethinking the process within traditionally procured road projects was reported by our respondents to be in the design and the procurement processes (see Table 5.2). Within PFI highways projects as these actually took form, such scope was reported essentially to be found on the construction side rather than the operations-related aspects of the project. The highest scores are reported in quality management, buildability and elimination of risk protection.

Our respondents recognised that the traditional way of procuring and designing the roads allowed scope for updating. Scope for innovations to increase speed of construction, reduce operating staff and introduce new construction and operating technologies were all also cited as important (see Table 5.3).

Savings achieved in the PFI highways projects

It is possible to affirm that in this sector PFI has been fairly successful in achieving cost savings, and savings are proportionately similar to those reported in the custodial sector. Important savings in construction costs have allowed total cost savings of about 10–15%, despite the large increase in costs reported in fees (see Fig. A.6 in

Appendix A.6). It must be added that there is no evidence to suggest that these increases in fees have reduced on more recent projects.

This finding seems, at first sight, to be consistent with other studies in the area of PFI road projects, including the NAO's report on the first four PFI road projects (NAO, 1998), which found similar levels of cost savings, on three of the four projects it reviewed. The NAO considered that the procurement process was competitive enough to give assurance that the terms obtained were the best obtainable from the market for deals of that type at the time. The transferred risks it considered to be substantial, especially demand or volume risk, although the use of shadow tolls was expected to have increased the cost of the projects to the Highways Agency, offsetting to some extent the benefits of placing other substantial risks appropriately. The NAO concluded that three of the four contracts examined would provide road projects on financially better terms than traditionally procured and conventionally funded alternatives.

On the fourth project reviewed by the NAO the absence of cost savings was attributed, by the NAO, to the low construction content of that project, which primarily involved the operation of an existing road.

It should be noted here that the NAO's study attempts to include financing costs in its comparison of PFI and public sector alternative costs. In this it differs fundamentally from our study. If PFI financing costs have in fact been substantially higher than the public sector cost of capital in road projects (where an 8% discount rate has been used for the PSC), then our findings would imply aggregate cost savings, including finance costs, substantially below those found by the NAO for its three 'successful' early projects.

Sources of innovation in PFI road projects

As in all sectors, the most common innovations in the PFI road projects are incremental. Furthermore, while some prototype solutions are reported, adaptations from other industries seem not to be important. However, adaptations from overseas construction are reported to be important. Presumably such adaptation has been assisted by inclusion of non-UK highway constructors and operators within some of the small number of leading PFI consortia in this sector (see Table 5.4).

Type of facility	Incremental	Prototype	Adapted from other industries	Adapted from non-UK construction	Adapted from non-UK operations
Total sample	4.3	2.8	2.6	2.1	2.0
Healthcare	4.5	2.5	2.9	1.7	1.5
Custodial	3.9	3.4	1.9	2.2	2.4
Roads	4.5	3.0	1.5	3.6	2.4

Table 5.4 *Relative importance of the ways of generating CSIs in the PFI projects of three sectors*

There is a clear agreement that a high proportion of innovations with technological roots constitutes the norm. It is probable that some of these technical innovations are being imported from construction industries abroad.

Furthermore, the kind of construction technology that is central in that innovation is also clear. There is almost unanimity in indicating that the use of new components and/or new materials is the key aspect. With regard to the areas of operations technology, the use of new components and/or new materials is also the main aspect

Area	Healthcare sector	Custodial sector	Highways sector
Scope for CSIs in traditional procurement	Basically: brief, design and procurement. Other stages also important	Basically: brief and operations. Some other stages also important	Basically: design and procurement. Some other stages also important
Scope for CSIs in the PFI project	Quality management, improving asset durability, improving operation staff efficiency, procurement (balance between operations and construction, average level for both)	Buildability, quality management, space planning, operation staff efficiency, procurement (balance between operations and construction, high level for both)	Elimination of excess risk protection, buildability, quality management (stress on construction)
Savings by stage of the PFI project	Large increases in fees have not been overcome on new projects. Largest savings in FM. Limited savings in construction costs. Savings are also reported on core operations. Poor total cost savings	Initial increases in fees already overcome. Similar savings in both construction and operation costs, allowing total cost savings between 10 and 15%	Important savings in construction costs, allowing total savings between 10 and 15%, despite large increases in fees
Sources of CSIs	Basically incremental solutions. Only a few prototype solutions and adaptations from other industries. No important adaptations from overseas	Most frequent are incremental solutions, but prototype solutions are also important. No important adaptations from other industries and some adaptations from other countries	Basically incremental solutions. Some prototype solutions. No adaptations from other industries. Evidence of adaptation from overseas construction industries
Technical roots of the CSIs	Basically non-technically based solutions	A mix of technically based and non-technically based solutions	Completely technically rooted solutions
Construction technology areas	Standardisation, prefabrication, communications IT applications (construction engineering)	Standardisation, prefabrication (construction engineering)	Use of new materials and new components (materials engineering)
Operations technology areas	Use of new equipment instead of personnel	Use of new equipment instead of personnel, and new monitoring techniques	Use of new materials and components
Reasons for the CSIs not to be applied before (expertise) Reasons for the CSIs not to be applied before (contractual)	Expertise existed in the industry but was not in use. Basically the organisational way of doing things within the NHS and, secondly, a lack of incentives to innovate	Expertise did not exist in the industry. Basically lack of incentives to innovate and, secondly, the organisational way of doing things within the Prison Service	Expertise did not exist in the UK road/construction industry. Restrictions from technical codes and norms
Kind of OS provided	Basically functional and performance specification, but with some design. The SPVs add more technical aspects	Only functional and performance specification. SPVs do not change that characteristic	Mix of performance and technical specification
Private sector evaluation of the OS	On average, between moderately appropriate and very appropriate	On average, moderately appropriate	On average, moderately appropriate
Reasons for the client to be unsatisfied with the OS	Basically lack of previous experience. Also interfaces between existing and new facilities	Basically complexity of the project	Basically time-scale of the contract and complexity of the project

Table 5.5 Summary of three-sector analysis

cited. It is therefore the case that in roads, the technical aspects of the engineering of materials are the cornerstones of the innovative activity.

Among the reasons why the implemented innovations were not applied prior to the PFI project, the non-existence of the necessary experience is not reported as an important explanatory factor (only around 30% of the respondents consider this to be a relevant point). Those respondents who did consider this factor to be relevant, identified the lack of expertise at the level of the industry or the country.

More than 50% of respondents reported that technical restrictions were highly relevant in explaining why innovations had not previously been applied. Restrictions in the form of technical codes or norms that hindered innovation were cited far more frequently and ranked as more important than contractual factors associated with risk, reward and incentive. It can therefore be concluded that a switch towards a less prescriptive or technical specification has been crucial for the kinds of CSI implemented in the PFI road sector. That transfer of technical risk has replaced management of risk via mandatory technical codes and norms seems to be unique to this sector. The PFI companies have, for example, been allowed to choose to reduce the depth of parts of the road pavement, on the basis that, if this in fact proves to be misguided and leads to shorter pavement life, it is they who will bear the consequent losses, in reduced 'lane availability' payments and increased reconstruction costs. This, again, highlights the importance of the technical aspects of the PFI road projects, an attribute shared with other kinds of PFI civil engineering projects.

As the starting point for the bidders from which to generate such innovation, they received fundamentally performance-technical OS, with a previously developed design. These designs were provided on the basis that the bidders could take them as they were, or they could modify them, maintaining or improving their quality standard, if considered appropriate or necessary. In this sense, the technical contents of the tender documentation remain very strong. There have, however, been efforts from the Highways Agency to transform those requirements into a more performance-type of requirement, in particular, with regard to operation specifications.

The principal difficulties that the clients and their advisers report at the time of producing those output specifications are related to difficulties of making contractual provision for uncertain future contingencies, relating to the very long time-scale of the contract and the complexity of the project itself. This seems to demonstrate that the vast experience and expertise of the Highways Agency allows it to focus on the contingent future dispute and reversion issues, characteristic of the theoretical discussion of the problems of long-term contracting.

5.5 Summary of similarities and differences

Table 5.5 summarises the issues examined in this chapter.

Chapter 6	# Case studies

6.1 Introduction

This chapter focuses on two quite different projects that have been procured using the PFI. An approach to the research based entirely on case studies was considered but rejected. Because of the large number of possible explanatory variables, and the number of dimensions in which PFI projects differ from one another, a survey approach was deemed preferable. The purpose of the case studies is therefore to demonstrate just part of the range of application and the ways in which the private sector has pursued this new opportunity.

The two individual studies have not been chosen because they are examples of either best practice or unsuccessful experiences. They were selected on consideration of their own very different characteristics as PFI projects, in order to illustrate how variable the PFI scenario can be. In both examples, it is argued that the public sector had a clear need for significant expenditure on capital assets to secure or improve its service provision to the public. For the sake of brevity, only certain aspects of the two cases are presented, and these have been carefully considered to fit within the scope of this research report. It is therefore accepted that other important features of both projects have been excluded, so that the emphasis can be placed on the issues pertinent to the analysis of the cost-saving innovations present. As some of the data were considered to be of a commercially confidential nature, the sections that follow are primarily descriptive.

The first case is the Stretford Fire Station in Greater Manchester. This case was selected to represent the smaller end of the range of size and complexity of PFI projects. A fire station can be considered not only as a potentially popular type of specific case in the future, but also as representative of a wider segment of the PFI market including, as well as fire stations, police stations, small custodial facilities and other highly purpose-specific buildings. Another central factor considered at the selection of this case was the architect-led character of the SPV, which might become a widespread norm in the future, at least for this kind of project.

The second case is the Queen Elizabeth Hospital in Greenwich. This case was selected after consideration of the complexity of the facility and the large size of investment (around £85m). It also represents a typical client of the healthcare sector – Greenwich Healthcare NHS Trust – and the SPV is a subsidiary of a large and experienced corporation with interests in different sectors of PFI.

6.2 Stretford Fire Station

Background

The Greater Manchester Fire & Civil Defence Authority (GMF&CDA) was created in 1986 and serves ten Metropolitan Fire Districts. The civil defence element of the authority's activities is currently very much reduced and therefore the responsibilities of the GMF&CDA are essentially fire-related.

GMF&CDA is a specialist organisation that derives its funding from local authorities through central government allocations, council tax and business rate revenues. As a self-accounting authority, the GMF&CDA is responsible for budget allocation, which includes the upkeep of its buildings. However, it has traditionally delegated to a Lead Authority provision for elements of its financial, legal and construction services. As part of the public sector, when the need for the new Stretford Fire Station was identified, the analysis of options carried out at the level of outline business case (OBC) determined that the only viable route to replace Stretford Fire Station would be PFI. This meant that the GMF&CDA would be responsible for implementing the project.

The organisational structure of GMF&CDA includes their headquarters, 5 divisional commands and 9 fire stations for each of those commands. In future, it is probable that the commands will be reduced to 3, managing about 14 stations each, equating to a total of 41 stations.

The current property portfolio of the Authority comprises 41 stations, a vehicle maintenance workshop, a supply department, 5 divisional buildings, the civil defence facilities, a training centre, a driving training school and the Fire Service Headquarters.

The two largest construction projects undertaken by the Authority in the recent past had capital costs of approximately £2.0m and £1.9m. Additionally, a series of smaller refurbishment projects have been carried out. In total, the capital building work sums up to about £8–9m during the past five years. The Authority's current investment profile requires instigating approximately the equivalent of one project of the characteristics of Stretford Fire Station per year. However, there are no available capital funds for such expenditure.

The scope of the present project is the replacement of Stretford Fire Station and the attached Divisional Headquarters building. Therefore, the project does not involve an increase in capacity. The HQ must provide a command, management and administrative function for `A´ Division, which serves the Metropolitan Borough of Trafford and the City of Salford. The statutory requirements for fire cover as set by the Home Office clearly demonstrate the need for a station at this location. The specified requirement is based on the need to provide the requisite speed and capability for attendance to incidents in the highest risk category covered by the station.

The reasoning behind considering procuring the project through PFI was a result of the continuous decrease in the availability of funds through the basic credit approval for the GMF&CDA. However, in the OBC, the considered options were as follows.

- *Do nothing.* Not considered further due to the imperative need to comply with the mentioned service standards
- *Do minimum.* The repair works would have reached a cost in excess of £1m and the facility would only have been able to cope with the operational requirements for a further 10 years, before more substantial improvements would have been required. This option required an investment of £1.08m plus the rebuild of the facilities in year 10 (£1.95m more), with a present value of the total costs of £6.87m.
- *Major refurbishment.* This solution would have addressed the structural condition

of the buildings and it was estimated that it would have given the existing facility a potential 20 years of further useful life. This option required an investment of £2.60m plus the rebuilding of the facilities in year 20, with a present value of the total costs of £7.50m.

- *New build.* This solution was considered the best as it would produce the least disruption, a facility estimated to last in excess of 40 years, a more flexible building, a purpose-designed office and command support facility and consequently a better service to the community. Two versions of this option were considered: using the existing site or a new site (both implied capital costs of about £3.5m). The present value of the total costs was £6.69m (existing site) and £6.74m (new site).

Resource requirements	Characteristics of the area
• Ideal placement for Divisional HQ for South Manchester, community activities (Fire Safety Work, Young Fighters Scheme, Community Watch Initiative) • Minimum 2 standard appliances, 1 aerial appliance, 1 reserve appliance • These dictate a four-bay station with watch strength of 16, watch station commanders, brigade and divisional managers • Standards of Fire Cover: reviewed in 1996, unlikely to be reduced and likely to increase even more • Required accommodation: dormitories, catering, rest rooms, offices, lecturing facilities, storage and locker rooms, catering, gymnasium, training tower	• Location: Borough of Trafford, 5 miles south-west of Manchester, adjacent to Trafford Park industrial estate • Largest concentration of fire risks in Greater Manchester, Trafford Park is predominantly 'A' risk (scale A to D) • £200m Trafford Centre Retail Park, a series of new industries in the area, continued growth in residential housing (about 10 000 new homes in last 20 years) **Characteristics of the old facility** • Built in 1939, bays are now too narrow, structural defects in brickwork and concrete, ad hoc alterations to accommodate personnel, Divisional HQ is inappropriately housed in a converted house, current facilities with serious safety and morale concerns **Characteristics of the new facility** • Capital costs: £3.2m (including fees) • Building area: four-bay station (1153 m²), Divisional HQ (368 m²) • Contract term: 25 years

Table 6.1 *General characteristics of the project*

From the analysis of the total costs against value, the solution adopted was to provide a fully serviced new building. For the calculation of the NPV of the total costs, a 25-year period, 8.8% rate of discount and 3% p.a. of inflation were considered. The business case then addressed the PFI procurement of such a project and compared it with a traditionally funded option (TFO) for a similar service.

Early in the process, the client set up a strategic reporting line. It comprised a Policy Sub-committee — constituted by six senior members of the GMF&CDA — which was empowered to approve the principal decisions of the project. Reporting to that, a Project Board — drawn from twelve senior members of the GMF&CDA — was in charge of the project. Meanwhile, a four-person working group was in charge of the day-to-day project management activities. Its members represented the Estates Department, Business Support, Operational Fire Fighters and the Legal Department.

The participant organisations

The participant organisations are shown in Table 6.2.

The client's team	The special purpose vehicle (SPV's) team
• Client: GMF&CDA	• SPV: PFF Stretford Ltd — 75% shareholding Carden Croft, 25% British Linen
• Operational adviser: In house	
• Financial adviser: Lead Authority Wigan MBC Treasurer + external verification from Secta	• Architect, building consultant and FM: Carden Croft & Co. Ltd
• Technical adviser: In house + external verification from WS Atkins	• Principal contractor: Snape Ltd
• Legal adviser: Lead Authority Wigan MBC	• Structural engineering and drainage design: Shaw Whitmore Fyffe Partnership
The funders' team	• Consulting M&E engineering: Miller Walmsley Partnership
• Funders: British Linen Bank plc	• Financial planning and tax: Howsons Chartered Accountants
• Accountants: Pannell Kerr Forest	• Legal advisers: Hill Dickinson Solicitors
• Monitoring, Surveyor & Technical Advisers: Currie & Brown	• Insurance advisers: Smithson Mason Group
• Legal advisers: Addleshaw Booth & Co	• Funding advisers: Property Finance International

Table 6.2 *The project team*

The SPV

Carden Croft & Co. Ltd (CC) was founded in 1995. It is an architectural practice and has 3 individual shareholders. It employs approximately 12–14 staff of whom about 8 are architectural. The projects accomplished by the practice cover a large range, from a £30m commercial development accomplished by the two principal partners as individuals, to examples such as a 300 000 ft^2 factory in Cambridge and workshops for Royal Mail. As a practice, it has experience of designing a range of building types and has a particular area of specialisation in commercial buildings.

CC became involved in PFI with the intention of diversifying from the normal architectural practice types of commission. CC sees architectural practice driving itself toward 'aesthetic design' in the built environment. CC sought longer-term contracts, leaving what it considered a decimated industry with poorer and poorer returns, combined with low growth in the market. The practice believes in a total concept of architecture and has been trying to introduce this concept, relating it to the total costs of the building over its life, as an alternative to simply considering the capital costs. However, it has been a difficult task as, typically, the people managing the capital investment have nothing to do with those running the building after commissioning. CC's experience has been that very few individuals and organisations relate the capital with the maintenance costs.

As PFI fits with these ideas, CC decided to develop facility management (FM) within its organisation and was happy to become involved in a 25-year contract, in order to achieve its financial objectives.

When originally involved in PFI, CC was looking at the health and education sectors. It recognised that it was targeting the £1–10m schemes – where it believed about 80% of the market would be found – rather than the mega-schemes; despite what the majority of those in the market at the time were saying, that PFI would not work for smaller projects. The results of its endeavours are that the practice has become involved in a project providing PFI services related to facilities other than the ones originally targeted, while keeping within the same range of capital Investment.

CC became involved in this project jointly with Snape – the principal contractor – with the idea of sharing the design and building responsibilities between them. And although CC's original idea was to take only a smaller share in the SPV, it finally held the majority equity.

The principal contractor

William Snape & Sons was a family business founded 120 years ago. It retained that characteristic until 1997, when the controllers of the company, headed by Mr Tony Snape, sold the company to Morgan Sindall.

The company – currently Snape Ltd – has carried out several projects in the range of £1–2m through their Medium Size Jobs Division that accomplishes projects over about £300 000. Another division – Smaller Projects – carries the projects up to approximately £250 000. It is therefore the case that the size of the Stretford Fire Station project is slightly larger than usual for the company.

Tony Snape became involved personally in the early days of the project, prior to the take-over of the family business. Snape expressed its interest in taking the responsibility for the building aspects of the project and discussed with Carden Croft the possibility of CC becoming the designer. To Snape, the project was only viewed as another source of building work and it did not take an equity stake in the SPV. It was CC who therefore took the whole responsibility for the 25-year operation through the SPV – PFF Stretford Ltd. CC holds 75% of the equity, initially equivalent to 6% of the capital costs of the project, while the funders provided 90% of those costs as senior debt and 4% as subordinated debt. The funders also held a 25% equity stake in the SPV.

The development of a PFI solution

Timetable

- Project identification: April 1996
- Committee approval to project submission: January 1997
- Appointment of advisers: December 1996–January 1997
- First drafts of technical and service requirements: January 1997
- Pathfinder approval: February 1997
- Advertise OJEC/local/national: March–April 1997
- Submissions evaluation (10):   May–June 1997
- OBC submission to Home Office: June–1997
- Issue invitations to negotiate (ITN):   July–August 1997
- Preliminary discussion with selected list: August–1997
- Refined technical and service requirements: October 1997
- Complete evaluation criteria: October 1997
- Complete contract documentation: November 1997
- Initial bids: December 1997
- Evaluation of bids: January–February 1998
- Final negotiations with preferred bidder: March–June 1998
- FBC submission to Home Office: June–1998
- Committee approval: July 1998
- Contract signed (scheduled):   September 1998
- Contract signed (actual):   December 1998
- Commissioning: 27 October 1999

It is important to recognise that this timetable was set up at the very beginning of the process by the client and was adhered to very tightly almost until contract signature. This is a factor that received positive comments, as it allowed the bidders to limit their costs to a minimum. Nevertheless, this does not mean that the process ran smoothly, as there were continual difficulties at each stage. They were, however, always solved in an effective way under a cooperative spirit that allowed the project to proceed. The only delay in relation to the original schedule was caused by the time overrun of the due diligence on the part of the bank, culminating in a delay of three months (see below) resulting in the contract being signed in December 1998 instead of September 1998.

The Process

Answering the OJEC publication, 41 enquiries or requests for a questionnaire were received, resulting in 10 expressions of interest. From these, 6 were shortlisted with 3 complying properly with the requirements – the minimum number needed to follow the PFI route. The pre-selection was therefore carried out without great concern by the client.

From the three final bidders, one would be classified as a national player – Bowmer & Kirkland Ltd – that had already secured the PFI contract for the Derbyshire Ilkeston Police Station. The second was a Scottish regional player – Portfolio Partnership – and the third was Carden Croft & Co. Ltd, who can be considered a regional actor in the North-west.

The process of bidding included three rounds of structured interviews with the different bidders on an individual basis. The first interview, conducted over a whole day, was in blocks of two hours for each bidder and had the objective of discussing the technical aspects of the documentation handed out three weeks before. The second round – two weeks after the first – included technical and financial matters of the bids. It was at these occasions that the opportunity arose to find out what the bidders were thinking of doing, and to have their doubts clarified. The final round of interviews – four weeks after the first – considered the technical, financial and legal aspects of the contract. From there on, the bidders had three weeks to present their proposals.

The competition and its results

The solutions from the different bidders were technically very similar. The reasons for this can be found in the nature of the facility. A fire station is a specialised building, but it can be considered as a very simple building incorporating some peculiar requirements.

The final design was a product of the client's involvement as well as the architect's. They worked very closely and an iterative process went on between the two of them. This constituted the key difference from the previous method of generating the designs. This approach was deemed valid as the concessionaire will have a commercial relationship with the client for 25 years.

Despite the bottom line of the proposals being very similar, there were considerable differences in the way in which the bids were constructed financially. Technically, the closest bid to the winning one comprised a larger building with, probably, more potential for problems and expenses. These eventual problems would be greatest at the time when the building would be handed back after the 25-year concession. This bid therefore appeared to involve more risk in the building and was also adjudged to be more heavily loaded on the management of the service provision.

Therefore, the client felt that any necessary changes would have been more costly.

The flexibility of the winning bid, reflected in a willingness to discuss and to reach an adequate solution on the part of the bidder as well as the responsiveness to the client's needs and way of working together, were all key issues in its selection. The fact that Carden Croft is a local actor and demonstrates a profound interest in getting involved in PFI also weighed in its favour. The long distance from the operation facilities of the other bidder, could, for example, have made the process more difficult. Additionally, as the other bidders were contractor-led consortia, they might have been more concerned with the capital investment, rather than the approach on low-maintenance-cost design adopted by the winner.

The final results of the competition (for the annual charge) were extremely close between Portfolio and Carden Croft, and at the same time, very close to the client's original estimations. In fact, in cash flow terms, the differences can only be appreciated in terms of indexation, timing and the split between availability and performance.

These figures were very close to the forecasts presented approximately twelve months before the deal was finally closed. In fact, the variation in the NPC of the adopted solutions was about £100 000 from the OBC to the full business case (FBC).

The costs of the bid assumed by the winning bidder reached approximately £140 000 to reach preferred bidder status. Of that, about £30 000–40 000 were direct costs and the rest can be accounted for as the time of the bidder's staff. To reach financial close, the preferred bidder had to invest in total nearly £250 000, essentially as a result of the legal and financial arrangements. It is interesting to comment that the estimate that the client had made of these figures was considerably lower than that from CC.

From the point of view of the client, the use of PFI still resulted in some residual financial risks. For that reason, a contingency account for £120 000 was established (a figure close to the usual 5% of the capital costs). At the time of conducting the fieldwork for this report (October 1999), the client had instructed less than £20 000 from this fund. This demonstrates that the variations have been very low, as a result of tighter control from the client and, therefore, less uncertainty in the final service. This can be attributed, among other reasons, to the centralised decision making within the client's organisation, therefore avoiding contradictory opinions among its parties and additional costs due to design modifications.

Design and construction

The OS basically comprised the so-called 'room datasheets'. These datasheets had the objective of analysing what GMF&CDA would need, putting together the requirements for each kind of room, such as: laundry, dormitory, garage, etc. They specified size, functionality, heating and lighting standards and other similar attributes, including the different elements constituting the room, such as the furniture, fixtures and fittings. These were detailed generic analyses of each room, but containing very limited technical specification of what the room had to provide. An example of these datasheets is shown in Appendix A.9. The client seems to have been aware of providing the scope for innovation in this respect. However, the actual innovation arising from this exercise does not appear to be important.

Furthermore, there was no preliminary design. The principal reason for this was the selection of the site. The original idea was to develop another site in the same area of the existing facilities, to commission the new facilities, to move into it and then to close down the original one (build on new site option). This would have guaranteed the least service disruption.

However, the area of Stretford is the subject of a large-scale redevelopment, causing a substantial rise in land prices. It was therefore decided to look for a provisional site, to redevelop the current site and then to move back (build on existing site option). However, the issue would become a matter of real concern for the success of the project. At a certain point in the process, this scheme required the public sector to have access to funds that did not exist in order to secure the provisional site, while the preferred bidder required a signed contract before acquiring it. The preferred bidder finally solved this difficulty, assuming an extra risk by signing the letting contract to secure the provisional site, while the legal and financial arrangements of the concession contract were still being finalised.

It must be added that this last issue is not a minor one. Having a chosen site in advance of the tender would have considerably simplified the bidding process. The search for alternative sites may create considerable extra costs for the bidders and, additionally, the situation could reach the point of creating an artificial market, if there were too few options, raising land prices even further. It is therefore considered that in cases such as this project, it seems more appropriate that the client secures the construction site in advance of the tender.

The solution finally adopted involved GMF&CDA keeping the ownership of the site and providing it on a leasehold basis to PFF Stretford Ltd for a period of 25 years. At the same time, the contract contained a sub-lease from PFF to GMF&CDA, for the use of the premises, with a reversion clause at the completion of the contract in year 25. To assure the positions, special conditions were set up to establish the state in which the facilities would be transferred at the end of the contract. Indeed, a maintenance fund would be accumulated throughout the contract, and after year 20, when the repayment of the debt would have been completed, an equal distribution of the profits from this fund would be made.

The role of the OS was significant, as it is a particular type of information that many non-PFI construction organisations would find novel. This is particularly relevant if it is considered that the OS was only a written document, with no drawings included.

The legal documentation, as acquired from a previous PFI project, sometimes had a tendency to use terminology that did not fit this case. It is possible to say that, bearing in mind the pathfinder nature of this project, this problem should be identified and solved for future schemes. It is the opinion of the principal participants that this should be possible. Otherwise, the continued use of the PFI procurement route would be seriously hampered.

Allocation of risks and payment mechanism

The services to be provided by the SPV include: building maintenance, ground maintenance, cleaning, caretaking and janitorial services, vehicle fuel storage, mechanical and electrical services, utilities, waste management, security, catering, furniture provision and renewal and life-cycle maintenance.

The risk register of the contract accounts for the following items.

- *Development and construction risks.* The SPV retained all the items of risk, except for late design or fire policy changes incorporated by the client and excessive interference of the client during construction, both of which are the client's responsibility.
- *Operating risks.* The SPV retained all the items of risk, except for the following: excessive costs of utilities, and operational problems produced by supply interruption of utilities, were responsibilities to be shared; surge of operational requirements due to a national disaster was a risk to be borne by the client.
- *Obsolescence risk.* The SPV retained all the items of risk, except for the following: specialist equipment failing to keep pace with change was a shared risk, while the emergence of larger fire appliances in the future was a risk borne by the client.
- *Regulatory and policy risks.* The SPV retained all the items of risk, except for the following: changes in construction legislation during construction period were a shared risk; late changes in design due to change in regulations regarding design, construction and equipment supply – including Home Office guidelines – were the client's responsibility; finally, the nationalisation, privatisation or merger of the client's organisation as well as lack of funds on the client's side due to a change in government policy were also risks to be borne by the client.
- *Economic risk.* The SPV retained several of the items of risk. However, there were a few items borne by the client, such as, terrorism, war, nuclear explosion, acts of God, changes in law specific to the fire service, early termination of contract due to non-contractual reasons and delay or failure to achieve financial close due to failure in performance of client's obligations or lack of clearance from Home Office and HM Treasury.

Figure 6.1 *General view of the new fire station from the training tower*

Therefore GMF&CDA only retains responsibility for the operation of the fire service and issues that are either only under the public sector control or absolutely out of control, such as war.

With regard to the payment mechanism, it has two main components: the availability component and the performance component. The former is an annual charge that is set out as a maximum payment minus penalties that are calculated according to the unavailability of zones. The zones are different areas of the facilities that are classified according to their priority of service. The main components of the availability definition are that the zone should be: sanitarily free from infestation, compliant with relevant health and safety legislation, heated, lit and equipped to OS requirements, and accessible, secure and free from disrepair. For each zone, a table of penalties is considered, according to their priority of service.

The performance component of payment penalises the SPV if the services are not performed to the pre-defined standard. Approximately 20% of the unitary charge is subject to performance defaults, although if performance falls significantly below an acceptable level, further deductions could result through failure to meet the availability criteria.

To monitor the performance of the service provider, the SPV and the client agreed a procedure. In this context, a 'user's representative' is appointed to act as a link between them. In order to provide the necessary information on which to base the regular payments, an FM report is presented by the SPV indicating the maintenance works to be carried out, the responsive maintenance tasks requested by the client and the failures in the provision of services.

If the capital costs are compared to the operation costs, it is possible to affirm that this project is located near the top limit of the range among PFI projects. In other words, the principal consideration, at the time of the risk evaluation, is the effect of the construction risks, rather than the operation-related ones. In fact, the only relevant operation risks refer to the hard FM. However, these risks, of course, can be controlled through a careful design process, which again brings the problem to the same construction risk minimisation exercise.

It is necessary to remember the minimum differences that the bids meant for the client, in terms of price. If these two factors are considered, it is possible to conclude that the principal objective achieved by the client was a reduction in the uncertainty level of the project, over the 25-year concession period, rather than the minimisation of costs for the procurement of the same project.

The cost-saving innovations achieved

The development of the Stretford Fire Station using the PFI route for procurement has not demonstrated remarkable examples of innovation, either of design, construction materials or construction techniques. Indeed, from the photographs of the project, as shown in Figs 6.1 and 6.2, it is clear that the solution to the output specification is a building that is of a familiar and common design and configuration.

Figure 6.2 Detail of the new fire station

The capital costs of design and construction are therefore similar to the values that would be achievable under other strictly controlled and well managed forms of procurement, such as design and build forms. However, the use of PFI has led to subtle differences that should become apparent over the course of the 25-year concession. An illustrative example of this is the analysis of options for the cladding of the building.

By taking a whole life cost approach, the architect and contractor considered the alternatives of proprietary sheet cladding systems and the use of traditional brick. Although the brick solution was recognised as slower to construct and more expensive in terms of the skill level needed, it was the preferred option as it has a longer life span, less risk of failure and a lower cost for ongoing maintenance and cleaning. In addition, on aesthetic grounds, the brick solution is more in keeping with the local environment.

This is an example of a series of higher-value investments that have been made. If procured as a D&B contract, the sheet-cladding solution might have been adopted, since it would probably have resulted in lower capital costs, at the expense of a higher whole life cost. Furthermore, this also illustrates why the cost savings seem to be absent in the project under the 'classical' perspective of a usual construction contract. It is by considering costs throughout the 25-year concession that the process of innovation becomes apparent.

Conclusions

The Stretford Fire Station is representative of a small project that has been undertaken by relatively small players. The project has achieved a robust solution to the problem faced by the client in a way that has transferred significant risk, improved the standard of facilities and achieved this without incurring a premium to the public sector. The actual cost savings made to date are acknowledged as being insignificant. For instance, the use of brickwork has increased the capital cost over the lowest priced alternative cladding option. However, the involvement of an architectural practice as the lead player in the concessionaire has brought significant benefit to the detailed consideration of what the building needs to provide so that the operational requirements of the client are achieved in a long-term, low cost way. The use of players who are local meant that lines of communication were short, problems could be resolved quickly and that the design solution was sympathetic with the locality. More importantly, this involvement has established an important bond between the concessionaire and the source of their PFI revenues. Although it is very early days for this particular concession, it is the intention of the concessionaire to keep in close contact with the day-to-day operations of the fire station and ensure that the hard and soft FM is provided to at least the minimum acceptable standards.

Given the size and scope of the Stretford fire station, there were few areas presenting significant opportunities to innovate. Areas that could be improved were primarily related to the cost and time saving that is possible during the bidding stage. As noted earlier in this case study, the need to go through the due diligence exercise increased the bidding costs and delayed the financial close by three months. While it is clearly necessary for the banks and institutions who will lend money to the project to satisfy themselves that the project is robust, on small projects such as this it would appear that a more nimble and interactive mechanism for completing due diligence may be a significant asset.

It can be argued that this project has many similarities to design and build. It is true that the physical product of this PFI project incorporates relatively standard design, material and construction solutions. This can be considered as optimising the functionality requirement of the output without additional aesthetic finesse, an often-noted feature of design and build. However, the consideration of low maintenance, configuration to ease facility management and support services and the level of understanding that has transpired from the conversations between the concessionaire and the client body all suggest that the initial benefits of design and build are augmented with a whole life cost approach and commitment to optimise the physical solution to ease operational costs and reduce ongoing costs.

6.3 The Queen Elizabeth Hospital

This second case study is a far larger and intrinsically more complex project than the Stetford Fire Station. For the purposes of this research only certain facets of the project are examined and a more general approach is taken. Thus, for example, a detailed account of the financing is not given here. (For readers who are interested in gathering more information on this project it is suggested that they refer to 'The PFI Awards 1999', published by the PFI Report, where the Queen Elizabeth Hospital PFI project is featured; and the Private Finance Initiative Journal, Sept./Oct. 1998, Vol. 4, No. 4, pp. 44–51). The following case study is intended to demonstrate both the complexity of the issues facing those who embark on using the PFI as a form of securing new facilities for the NHS and how the private sector can contribute to solutions that are new to this type of facility.

Background

The Queen Elizabeth PFI Hospital is due to open in May 2001 and will provide the residents of the London Borough of Greenwich with state-of-the-art healthcare on a site previously occupied by the Queen Elizabeth Military Hospital (QEMH) adjacent to Woolwich Common in south-east London.

The motivating force behind this 571-bed PFI hospital (including 87 mental health beds, 11 critical care beds and 28 day-care beds) was the requirement of Greenwich Healthcare NHS Trust (henceforth: the Trust) to rationalise its primary hospital service provision and to tackle the problems created by the running of its existing stock, principally involving Greenwich District Hospital (GDH).

The allocation of healthcare provision is a complex subject and a full analysis falls outside the remit of this study. However, the decision to be made in the case of Greenwich's proposal for a new hospital involved the District Health Authority (Bexley and Greenwich Health Authority) and the wider community of the London teaching hospitals, including Guys and St. Thomas' and Kings College. The factors present included the way in which healthcare is provided and this itself is a complex and changing area of expertise. There is a general reduction in bed spaces resulting from more day-care surgery, the development of specialist treatments in clinical centres requiring the movement of patients between locations, and more advanced treatments available from General Practitioners and out-patient departments.

The provision of healthcare in Greenwich is relatively typical of many established urban areas, with a long history of local hospitals and health facilities, some of which have now closed and others that are continuing to operate. The most significant hospital within the borough is GDH, a deep plan, concrete framed structure started in the late 1960s and fully completed in the mid-1970s. GDH is now the primary hospital for the Borough of Greenwich following the closure of the Brook hospital in the mid 1990s and the winding down of the Memorial hospital. GDH is less than 30 years old, but suffers from problems of large concrete and steel structures built at that time. It is an imposing concrete framed structure that has proved to be expensive both to run and maintain. During its life there have been many partial refurbishments and feasibility plans to expand its capacity, including a scheme in the late 1980s to add an additional floor to the building. With increasing demand for NHS services and a limited budget,

Greenwich has been forced to make difficult choices in the way that it allocates its budget. One long-term consequence of the limitation on funds has been that there is an accumulation of maintenance required at GDH that was estimated in excess of £30 million at November 1996. This had increased to £32 million by November 1998. This escalation in maintenance backlog costs at GDH of an additional £1m p.a. is due to the additional load placed on the building while patient services have been temporarily transferred from other of the Trust's hospitals.

The Borough of Greenwich is home to the Royal Artillery, which has a substantial presence around Woolwich Common. This significant military community also included the QEMH. This was designated as an army hospital, although during the 1990s it received an increasing number of civilian referrals as closer links were established with the NHS Trust through the creation of an internal market in the NHS. Following a review by the MoD of its medical needs, a combined forces hospital was established in Hampshire, with the Woolwich site being made redundant. This resulted in the need to dispose of the QEMH complex. As the QEMH was more modern and was based on a steel structure, it was seen to offer fewer building-related problems than GDH and was identified by the Trust as offering a potential solution to their increasing problems. The identification of the QEMH as a site for a NHS hospital was therefore established in the early 1990s and, indeed, the acquisition of QEMH took some of the patient load from the Brook Hospital, which allowed it to close and be sold as a site for conversion to residential use.

Participant organisations

The principal players involved in the development of the Queen Elizabeth PFI Hospital are the Trust, the Trust's advisers (KPMG), the SPV (Meridian Healthcare) and the principal supplier to the SPV, Kvaerner plc. Of significance to this case study are also the role of HealthCare Projects who acted as consultants to the SPV (former senior NHS personnel who have formed an independent advisory consultancy), the architect to the contractor (The George Trew Dunn Partnership), Kvaerner Rashleigh Weatherfoil, who are the design consultants, installers and 'hard' facility managers for the mechanical, electrical, public health and IT elements, and ISS who provide the 'soft' facility management services. There are, in addition, a significant number of other financial and legal players who acted as advisers or suppliers of more specialist services. A list of some of these players and their role is given in Table 6.3.

The client's team	The SPV's team
• Client: Greenwich Healthcare NHS Trust • Legal adviser: Herbert Smith • Financial advisers: KPMG	• SPV: Meridian Healthcare • Shareholders: Kvaerner Corporate Development, Innisfree (Meridian) • Financial adviser: Kvaerner Financial Services • Legal advisers: Clifford Chance
	The funders' team • Bond underwriters: Barclays Capital • Legal advisers: Allen & Overy • Credit rating agency: Duff & Phelps

Table 6.3 Principal players in the Queen Elizabeth Hospital PFI project

Development of a PFI solution

The Trust recognised that they needed to resolve the increasing problem of affording to provide modern healthcare services in the borough of Greenwich. As their existing stock of buildings were either very old (the Brook and Memorial) or expensive to run and maintain (GDH) an ever greater proportion of their budget had to be spent on their building stock. An independent review of healthcare provision in Outer London in 1994 recommended the need for two major acute hospitals in the south-east Thames corridor and that one of these hospitals needed to be sited in Greenwich. In accord with this report and in line with the regional and national strategy for the provision of healthcare, the QEMH was purchased from the MoD in August 1995. This purchase allowed the running down of services at the Brook Hospital, which subsequently closed and has now been converted to provide a variety of housing units. This asset sale was made part of the subsequent PFI deal. The newly acquired hospital was required to retain its name, but was simplified to Queen Elizabeth Hospital (QEH).

The Trust considered the question of using PFI and decided to proceed with this procurement route from an early juncture. An OBC was submitted in March 1995. The notice in the OJEC appeared in April 1995, before the purchase of the QEMH was completed. The response led to the identification of a short-list and ultimately to the identification of a preferred bidder (Meridian Healthcare), which was a consortium led by Trafalgar House (subsequently owned by Kvaerner SA of Norway).

During the process of selecting the preferred bidder and developing the scope of the project, a critical question is whether the contract between the public sector client and the concessionaire will contain sufficient risk transfer to allow the project to move from the public sector's balance sheet to that of the private sector. In the absence of standard contracts that automatically resolve this very complex question there was, at the time, a great deal of effort expended in identifying the criteria that such transference would be measured against. In this context the role of advisers is critical, and in this case, the Trust's original advisers were concerned that the contract as it was emerging was not capable of passing this critical test. This view was based upon a perception and clearly there will be times when different perceptions exist about the same phenomenon. Such a situation developed, and this culminated with the Trust choosing to appoint new financial advisers (KPMG) in February 1997. KPMG appraised the situation and drew on their experience of working on the Dartford and Gravesham Hospital PFI project and the work carried out on the other four pioneer PFI hospital projects. The result was a favourable report where KPMG were highly optimistic that the Trust could propose a PFI contract for the provision of a new hospital that would transfer sufficient risk to the concessionaire, allowing the hospital to move off the Trust's balance sheet. In preparation for this, KPMG worked with the Trust to prepare the necessary documentation to be presented to HM Treasury. This included the draft contract and the documentation forming the backbone of the public sector comparator. The two principal components of the PSC were the consideration of the complete refurbishment of the QEH and the subsequent decanting of the Memorial and GDH, together with the 'do minimum' option, which meant doing the critical work necessary on GDH and continuing to use the Memorial Hospital. For both these alternatives there were significant drawbacks that led to both higher (and potentially increasing) costs as well as sub-optimal services provision.

The Queen Elizabeth PFI Hospital involved extensive building work and was therefore subject to planning consent. A public enquiry was held in April/May 1996 and planning permission was granted in March 1997. Given the pre-existing hospital, the most major concern for planning approval was the need for increased car parking space. The application for the hospital was approved; however, the full application for car parking spaces was rejected. This, at the time of writing, leaves the hospital with several hundred fewer car parking spaces than was hoped for. This will mainly affect hospital staff, who will have to use other forms of transport, primarily public buses to get to and from the facility.

During this period, the Trust and its advisers worked on developing the FBC. This was submitted to central government in January 1997 and was in the process of review when the government changed in May 1997. There was an immediate hiatus on PFI while Sir Malcolm Bates carried out his review. Following this, the NHS established a prioritisation exercise that ranked proposed PFI projects in terms of the strategic need, appropriateness to fit the use of PFI and degree of development of the proposal. The Queen Elizabeth PFI Hospital proposal was initially ranked fifteenth in this exercise, suggesting that it would not be part of the first wave of PFI hospital projects. However, the scheme continued to progress with the Trust producing a response to the prioritisation exercise in July 1997. For this there was a concentration of effort on clarifying the proposed contract conditions to meet the government's objectives of PFI becoming more straightforward with wider use of standard contracts. By October 1997 the Queen Elizabeth PFI Hospital had moved up the prioritisation list and was sanctioned to proceed, with a revised FBC being developed. Before the revised FBC was submitted, the final report of the London Review on Healthcare was published in January 1998, which stated that [they, the Report's authors]:

"were very impressed with the planning, preparation and consultation which had been undertaken to put forward this scheme. Collaboration between agencies was well advanced. We support this development."

In addition, there was significant political support for the scheme by the local MP, Nick Raynsford, and the Health Secretary at the time, Frank Dobson. These powerful political voices would have created a backdrop that was positive for the scheme's consideration.

The final version of the FBC was submitted in April 1998 and received full authorisation to proceed soon thereafter.

The project that was signed off was for a new acute district hospital with 571 beds (consistent with the FBC). This was scaled down from the original proposal due to the Regional Health Authority's concerns about overall bed numbers to be provided within the region. This change, in part a reflection of the London Review carried out in late 1997, reduced the scale of the project after negotiations with the preferred bidder had commenced and therefore had to be accommodated in the final contract.

This reduction in the size of the project was part of a thorough evaluation by the Trust and the Regional Health Authority of the provision of services in this part of London. The situation is reasonably complex, as patients can be relatively easily referred to specialist services provided by the large teaching hospitals in London, located at Guys, St. Thomas' and Kings College. To optimise the service provision at the QEH site, it was therefore necessary to consider what services were to be provided and how they would operate as part of a whole NHS 'system'. Establishing this set of requirements is critical for the development of the OS which, in the case of hospitals, involves highly detailed information including data necessary to allow the generation of room datasheets that list all the functional requirements for each designated spatial unit. (These would be similar to the type of information presented in Appendix A.9 from the Stretford Fire Station project.) The result of this operation was a dialogue between the Trust managers of the PFI project and the various clinical and non-clinical departments who would be involved in the new hospital. This set of discussions was then fed directly into the negotiations with the concessionaire, who had the responsibility of designing, building, financing and operating the PFI hospital.

This led to an intense period of discussion and negotiation, in which the teams from the Trust and Meridian had to clarify ownership of specific risks, detailed requirements for the functioning of the building and agree a contract that was acceptable to both parties. During the initial stages of the PFI project there was a comprehensive re-evaluation of the project by Meridian and the design for the hospital changed significantly as a result of the detailed review of the requirements which was carried out and constraints that were being imposed.

During the course of the negotiations, the principals of the contract agreed the terms in an everyday language and then instructed their various representatives to convert this 'everyday agreement' into an appropriate form to be entered as part of the contract. Another important point was the inclusive nature of discussions, with all interested parties present. This meant, for example, that both the hard and soft FM companies had representatives present during design meetings. This enabled all parties to gain a 'flying start'.

One further important consideration was the need to have the new hospital operational as soon as possible. This requirement was driven by the need to vacate the QEH for the duration of the building works and to relocate services to the GDH and Memorial. Given the state of these existing sites, the additional imposed workloads meant pushing the space utilisation, administrative systems and building fabric and services to capacity. This is far from ideal, as it constrains options when things go wrong (which, given the age of buildings and equipment and poor layouts, is likely). Therefore, it was critical to both the Trust for operational reasons and the concessionaire for contractual and financial reasons to achieve the opening of the new hospital at the earliest opportunity. Given that the existing QEH was to be used as the base for the new hospital, the risks associated with refurbishment were substantially reduced by only reusing 30% of the existing elements of the main hospital building (the other 70% were demolished) and where the existing structures were reused, stripping them back to the structural steel frame. In addition to the main hospital building, there is another significant structure on the site. This is a relatively small concrete framed block (Ranken House) and the proposal involving the PFI hospital designates an existing tower block building as doctors' residential accommodation and therefore requires a complete internal refurbishment and upgrading of services. Given the nature and scope of the work, and the possibility that there may be structural problems with the concrete frame and the likelihood of the use of asbestos throughout the structure, this element of the project poses significant challenges. In the wider context of the PFI project, the Trust decided to exclude the Ranken House element of the works from the PFI project. It was hoped that this would minimise the delays to the operational status of the completed hospital and reduce the risk premium that this addition would warrant from the concessionaire.

Design and construction

The design of the new Queen Elizabeth PFI Hospital follows the footprint of the existing structure, originally used as a military hospital. The layout of departments is, however, different and is the result of the thorough review of the way in which NHS services are provided. Of most interest are, first, the location of the pharmacy, which was identified as being best placed in a central position to allow both out-patients and in-patients to be served effectively and efficiently. Second, the transmission of images from X-rays, MRI and CAT scans are in digital format, negating the need for large archive spaces in the long term, but increasing the need for IT network provision within the hospital, through a system known as PACS. Third, the main entrance was reviewed in a cost-cutting exercise and is now less grand than originally envisaged.

During the design development there was a need to translate the

Figure 6.3 and 6.4
Cladding panels of the Queen Elizabeth PFI Hospital [Source Kvaerner Construction]

detailed operational requirements from the NHS users into a brief that could be interpreted by the architects and engineers. This translation of technical requirements was made significantly easier for the concessionaire through the appointment of HealthCare Projects. The use of such consultants enabled a medically or clinically technical dialogue to take place during the negotiation process, with the output from this being translated for the concessionaire by their consultants. This allowed for rapid appreciation of requirements and relatively quick iterations in design solutions. In addition, all significant meetings that discussed operational requirements were attended by the integrated M&E design, installation and 'hard' FM company as well as the 'soft' FM provider. The issue of the facility management was critical to the PFI project, as the risk transference requirements meant that all of the complex FM issues had to be identified, clarified and provided for as part of the PFI contract. This involved the Trust's Head of Facilities with his team and the concessionaire's designers and facility managers and placed great pressure on all those involved to agree acceptable solutions.

The design solution intrinsically adopts a modular approach to both the architecture and services. The layout of the new PFI hospital is on a 3 m grid and the façade is dominated by modular cladding panels. The cladding on the project is particularly interesting, as it is believed to be the first time that the system has been used in the UK. The components for the cladding panel arrive on site and are assembled on one of three purpose-made assembly beds. These beds are enclosed, enabling assembly of the relatively large panels to be carried out regardless of weather conditions, and in controlled conditions that ensures their performance. Figs 6.3 and 6.4 illustrate the design of the cladding panels.

Internally, there is use of prefabrication and modularity. Pre-finished plastic coated aluminium conduits are used, wiring is designed on a modular basis to simplify and speed installation and metal pipework has proprietary crimped ends to ensure quick connections.

As the concession for the PFI hospital is 30 years, the long-term performance of the structure and equipment was a significant factor in the design and specification of the building and its components. The building has therefore been designed for operational reliability, ease of maintenance and low running costs. This has led to a standardisation of components, elimination of complex design solutions and the specification of thermally efficient materials and components.

Cost-saving innovations achieved

The new Queen Elizabeth PFI Hospital represents a project that is, at the time of writing, regarded as a significant success. The contract agreed and signed is seen as a major step towards a standard contract for PFI hospitals. The financial arrangements, using index-linked bonds (for a more detailed explanation of the financial tools used on this project see The Private Finance Initiative Journal, Issue 4, Vol. 3, Sept./Oct. 1998), was an effective method of finance that was relatively cheap as well as being relatively quick and straightforward to arrange.

The innovations on this project can be classified under three broad headings. The first would be the organisational innovations. Here, the innovations that resulted from the use of PFI were at three levels. First, there was the opportunity for the Trust to integrate the various departments that are involved in operating a district hospital. Given the background to this case study, the Trust used the challenges set by PFI to effectively re-

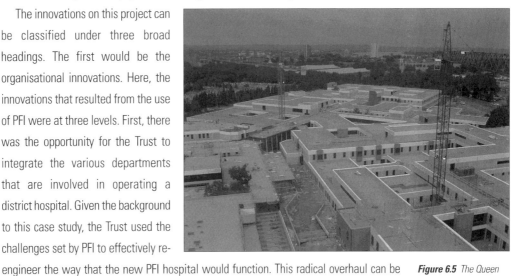

Figure 6.5 *The Queen Elizabeth PFI Hospital during construction [Source Kvaerner Construction]*

engineer the way that the new PFI hospital would function. This radical overhaul can be considered as being driven only by the fundamentally different approach that PFI requires. The integration of provision of NHS delivered services in the new hospital are therefore expected to set new levels for this type of hospital. Second, the way in which the Trust and the various component parts of the concessionaire negotiated the contract were based on a highly driven motivation to succeed. The definition of success would clearly be defined differently for the two parties but, in total, the Trust and the concessionaire were able to use this motivation to foster a relationship that moved away from adversarial, to a more trusting and cooperative form. The negotiations were bolstered by the inclusion of a firm of specialist consultants familiar with the NHS operational requirements. To ensure that this was a secure route of progression, a very clear and highly effective contract was drawn up and agreed. Third, the role that Kvaerner took can be considered as highly unusual, with a single parent company being responsible for the structural and architectural design, services design, installation and hard FM. The involvement of other key suppliers during design development continued this inclusive approach.

The second area of innovation is the use of technical innovations. Here there are two main areas. The first is the use of the cladding system that is cheap, thermally efficient and reliable. As it arrives in component form, is assembled under relatively controlled conditions into elemental form on a just-in-time basis and then installed quickly, it appears to offer the various certainties of cost, time and performance that are sought. On the services side, the use of modularity, pre-finished components and standardised systems are all examples of a careful trade-off between capital cost, ease of installation and the long-term performance criteria for the items. In a hospital context, it is reasonable to anticipate that the services will have to be capable of adaptation, regular maintenance and replacement. With service payment penalties levied for sub-standard performance, there is an imperative that failures are avoided or rapidly rectified.

The final area of innovation is the financing of the PFI project through the use of bonds. This area of innovation, with the Queen Elizabeth PFI Hospital being the first hospital project to succeed in using index-inked bonds, opens up possibilities for other PFI projects of a similar nature.

Conclusions

The Queen Elizabeth PFI Hospital project hospital project moved from one of many proposed to one of few to succeed because it received committed and concentrated input from a range of individuals and organisations that believed that the case for the PFI hospital was fundamentally sound. The Trust's client team comprised key individuals and organisations that understood the issues involved in PFI and who worked together to progress the project and resolve problems. Mirroring them were the team from the preferred bidder, with a core drawn from Kvaerner (formally Trafalgar House) and who were backed by their advisers. One of the most significant findings from this case study was that the key to the project's success (it was awarded *PFI Healthcare Project of the Year*, 1998) was the involvement of a committed, knowledgeable and integrated set of teams from both the Trust and the SPV. It was evident that to achieve the success alluded to so far, required a very high level of involvement for a sustained period. There were no remarkable circumstances that led to this project being successful, indeed there were occasions where gaps emerged between the concessionaire's position and that of the Trust. The outcome was always to converge and this was achieved through a working relationship between the Trust and its advisers and the concessionaire and its advisers. A cornerstone of this relationship was the trust that developed which led to openness during the negotiations. Although a significant issue at the time, the degree of agreement can be gauged from the most significant sticking point, which was about the risk of nuclear fallout.

The Queen Elizabeth PFI Hospital can be considered as a successful PFI project to date. The achievements that this project has made, both in terms of the particular problems solved and in terms of presenting a model for other similar projects to follow, are highly significant. Given the challenges that such a technical facility has to solve and the focus on achieving value for money, it is not surprising that the appearance of the building is not of high architecture, but of a more functional design. However, the standard of finish and the quality of facility should make the hospital a far better environment for patients to be treated and staff to work in. Critically, this standard should not be subject to the gradual decline that has historically befallen NHS procured and provided hospitals. Here, the standard set will be ensured, or indeed possibly improved, over the course of the concession, to the long-term benefit of all concerned.

From a purely PFI perspective, it is highly significant to note that the existing structure was seen more as a strategic opportunity to resolve a crisis, rather than a practical physical solution. The existing facilities were largely demolished as being liabilities or sources of potential risk. The project offers the client considerable value for money. The absolute value achieved through providing the solution using PFI was demonstrably better than any of the alternatives considered and the public sector client and indeed the local public who will use the facility will benefit from a carefully considered and integrated solution that provides healthcare facilities of a notably higher standard than the NHS was previously capable of providing.

6.4   Conclusions to the case studies

The case studies of Stretford Fire Station and the Queen Elizabeth PFI Hospital have revealed how PFI has been used to solve critical problems for public sector clients. This has been achieved in a way that has allowed them to channel the energies of private sector players into providing solutions that are felt, by those concerned, to be significantly better than would have been provided under the old forms of public sector procurement. Critically, the financial tests imposed by using the PFI have meant that the solutions that have been secured have been achieved without imposing a significantly higher cost on the public exchequer.

The complexities of the projects are clearly related to their size and function, but what appears to be common to both these projects is that they have achieved the level of success acknowledged to them by the commitment of both the public sector client and the concessionaire. On the larger Queen Elizabeth Hospital there was a raft of advisers and specialists who were also involved, but the research team received the impression that it was the positive force provided by both principal parties that drove the project to successful conclusion of the deal. In the case of the Stretford Fire Station, the project is crucial for the local community and the players are drawn form this area and clearly contribute a significant element of 'local knowledge' which has meant that problems are quickly identified and resolved, dialogues are frequent and a 'can do' philosophy was developed. This last point is probably the most crucial conclusion to be drawn from the information presented in these two case studies. It is clear that successful PFI needs to foster an environment between the principal players which leads to a requirement to work with each other rather than against each other. It has been shown through the two case studies that important decisions have been taken when there were significant risks present. To counter the opportunism that could have existed, the solution was to develop a trusting relationship, following commercial principles, where the progress of the project was improved without undue harm being inflicted on either of the parties. Such mutual benefits, known to economists as Pareto-superior, are at the heart of the sentiments in the Egan Report and should be seen as a critical success factor when using the PFI.

Chapter 7

Conclusions and recommendations

7.1 Key findings and conclusions

Conclusions regarding cost savings reported, all projects

- The median reported design, build and operate (DBO) cost saving is between 5% and 10% (Chapter 3, Section 3.4).
- The range of reported DBO cost savings is from a maximum of over 20% (three projects in the survey) to a minimum of between 10% and 20% increase (two projects in the survey) (Appendices A.6 and A.8).
- Just over one-third of respondents reported DBO cost savings of 10% or more (Appendices A.6 and A.8).

We conclude that, especially on the two-thirds of the projects surveyed with savings reported in DBO costs of less than 10%, savings achieved by adopting PFI must be judged to be disappointing against the optimistic targets of the Egan Report, for 10% savings per annum.

It appears that, though there are positive value for money (VFM) achievements, the PFI process has accomplished something less than a dramatic rethinking of design, construction and operation in most PFI projects to date.

We confirm the NAO's view that there is 'extraordinary variation between different deals', not only in the extent of cost saving and amount of innovation, but also in the content, process and circumstances of those deals.

We found a lower average level of reported cost saving than in the sum of NAO reports to date, or than in the Andersen/LSE Report. Although our methodology is not directly comparable with those reports, we believe that reasons for the difference include the following.

- NAO reports to date have mainly covered prisons and highways – two types of project for which we did find levels of saving not necessarily inconsistent with the DBO savings implied by the NAO findings for design, build, finance and operate (DBFO) savings.
- Further research would be required to make a direct estimate of financing cost dissaving in each PFI project, or to include more projects of other types in the NAO's coverage, before one could comment further on the consistency or otherwise of our findings with those of the NAO.
- The Andersen/LSE Report is confined to projects for which a public sector comparator was available. These may not be a representative selection of the entire population of PFI projects – indeed they are likely to over-represent centralised clients' projects.

Conclusions regarding cost savings reported, by type of project (Chapter 4)

DBO cost savings are modest in most types of PFI project, but they are:

- significantly higher in custodial and transport projects
- significantly higher in projects with centralised clients
- significantly higher in projects in which the PFI company provides a complete service, including core service
- significantly higher in projects based on the application of civil engineering technology.

DBO cost savings are not significantly higher in PFI projects that:

- are larger than average
- have pure performance-based output specifications (OS) or no technical content to their OS.

Thus, two of the four factors proposed to explain variation in cost saving work as expected (centralised clients; complete service); two do not (size of project; form of OS); while one unexpected factor (civil engineering-based) is important.

Taking the three factors with strong positive associations with cost saving in turn, and then looking at them in combination, we think the reasons why these factors matter are as follows.

Centralised clients

It is clear that experience of the client organisation is, in itself, significant, but that this is reinforced if embedded in a programme of similar projects, successively procured by the same public sector procurement agency, such as HM Prison Service or the Highways Agency.

Civil engineering based

These projects seem to permit and encourage a more focused and a more technological approach to the search for cost saving innovations (CSIs), and this seems to pay off in higher cost savings.

We note that civil engineering based projects have been among the most successful in terms of cost savings despite being the main ones to carry substantial 'demand risk', as embodied in the system of shadow toll payments for roads, or off-take agreements for utilities, and that one would expect this risk bearing to have caused PFI prices to be somewhat higher than they would otherwise be.

Complete service content

The two key aspects of this factor appear to be: the absolute scope of the content of the PFI contract (the amount and range of operating services that are included); and the relative scope of the PFI contract as a proportion of the total services involved in providing final services to the project users.

Highways PFI contracts rank high in terms of the latter (relative scope) but not of the former (absolute scope). On the other hand, custodial PFI contracts rank high in scope in both senses, while education PFI contracts rank low in scope in both senses.

Where a PFI contract ranks low in relative scope, we think that the process of output specification and the bidders' confidence in their ability to innovate effectively and control the risks involved therein may be the locus of difficulty.

It also seems clear that where a centralised client has, or group of decentralised clients have jointly, formed a clear view about the general direction of desirable change in operating regime, there is likely to be more success in cost saving (as in prisons) than where no such view exists (as, we think, in education).

Factors in combination

In fact, many projects which fell into one of the effective categories also fell into others. Thus, for example, a high proportion of civil engineering based projects (including almost all highways projects) were to provide a complete service to a centralised client; similarly custodial projects were to provide a complete service to a centralised client.

The present data set is not large enough to permit us to disentangle the independent influence of each factor in the absence of the others. The distribution of characteristics of the population of PFI projects is such that something approaching a 100% census of projects with the relevant characteristics would be required to do so with full statistical confidence.

Where any two of the effective explanatory factors are present, benefits are compounded. In the absence of all three, benefits are likely to be negligible. Thus, for example, if we consider a putative building-based, FM-only service content project for a decentralised client, we would predict that the chance of achieving successful DBO cost savings on such a project would be very low. Unfortunately, a substantial proportion of the potential PFI market possesses this combination of characteristics.

Conclusions regarding cost savings reported, by type of cost (Chapter 3, Section 3.4)

Over all projects, the percentage median cost savings reported were:

- total costs: savings of 5-10%
- construction costs: savings of 5-10%
- FM costs: savings of 5-10%
- core operating costs: savings of 5-10%
- preliminary costs: 5% saving to 5% increase
- other fees: increases of 10-20%

The 'weights' of these components of cost are unequal on average, and vary substantially from project to project. Overall, construction costs seem to have the highest average weight, i.e. account for the highest single proportion of total DBO costs.

The highest reported percentage construction cost savings were in transport projects, and the lowest in education and accommodation projects. The highest reported percentage core operations cost savings were in custodial projects, and the lowest in education projects. The highest reported percentage facility management cost savings were in custodial projects, and the lowest in transport projects. The lowest reported increases in fees were in custodial projects, and the highest in transport and healthcare projects.

The Andersen/LSE study contains the suggestion that percentage cost savings might be higher, over all projects, in construction than in operating costs because it found an association between percentage total cost saving and percentage of construction cost in total cost.

There is also an argument that, in conventionally financed public sector projects, the standard of provision of some operating services, and especially of facility operations, tends to decline over time, because of inadequate budget provision for maintenance. It is also argued that, in PFI contracts, there are sufficient financial incentives in the mechanism linking payments to service quality to prevent this from happening. PFI companies, it is argued, therefore allow and cost for a higher level of maintenance. This would then mean that an 'operations' value-for-money comparison would give a different result to that of a simple cost comparison. In effect, the argument is that, in their benchmarks, respondents will have estimated public sector operating costs as the costs of providing a slowly deteriorating standard of facility services.

If the above argument is correct, one would then expect to find a lower percentage reported saving in facility management costs than in other types of cost.

We did indeed find a slightly lower set of reported percentage cost savings in FM than in construction and core operations. However, the difference was very slight, and did not meet the tests for statistical significance.

Conclusions regarding inefficiencies in traditional procurement and provision (Chapter 3, Sections 3.2 and 3.3)

Pre-PFI procurement and provision was regarded as relatively efficient by respondents in transport, healthcare, accommodation and housing projects, and as least efficient by respondents in custodial projects. This seems to explain, in large part, why custodial PFI projects report among the highest CSIs and cost savings, but it makes the outcome for transport projects more surprising.

Conclusions regarding innovation (Chapter 3, Section 3.5)

Innovations in civil engineering projects are reported to be mainly technological, whereas innovations in building projects are much less frequently technologically based.

This may explain, in large part, why civil engineering PFI projects report among the highest levels of CSIs and cost savings. It suggests that incentive to innovate is not enough. It helps greatly if there are also identified focused opportunities for innovation, such as those to introduce new pavement materials in highways.

A focus opportunity requires that:

- there is an area on which search for innovation is focused because it accounts for a high percentage of the total
- there is technological opportunity, arising from new technical knowledge or innovations made elsewhere, to reduce costs of this focus area substantially.

Most important innovations had been generated at brief or concept design stage (Chapter 3, Section 3.5). This corresponds with the invitation to negotiate (ITN) stage in PFI projects. Innovation in a context of competitive bidding raises some particular issues, above all the risk that innovation-seeking expenditure of time and effort will have to be written off as a loss if the bid is unsuccessful. Since the costs of involvement in a PFI bid are in any case relatively high, there may be an understandable reluctance to increase these still further.

The intensity of competition in PFI bidding may be highly variable between sectors and types of project. If the other firms short-listed for a project are thought likely to search for innovation, then any bidder who decides not to search for innovations must recognise that their chance of being the winning bidder will thereby be greatly reduced.

The role of competition may well be crucial in stimulating innovation in this context. In particular, it may be that innovation occurs more in response to pressure to improve the bidder's chances of winning the bid than in response to the size of the extra profit expected from the innovation should the bid be successful.

The place of innovation in the bidding strategies of PFI firms would be worth further specific research.

Conclusions regarding appropriateness of PFI processes

(a) Only one quarter of SPV respondents rated the clients' OS as 'highly appropriate'. In 40% of cases these respondents thought that the OS used were still at least in part 'technical' or prescriptive (Chapter 3, Section 3.6). Despite this strong private sector opinion that such specifications are less appropriate, we found no clear relationship between the form of OS and the extent of cost saving (Chapter 4, Section 4.6 and Appendix A.8).

(b) Public sector responses were divided in their levels of satisfaction with the process and product of writing OS. Centralised clients were mainly satisfied with what they were able to achieve, and regarded the main unsolved problem as the inherently intractable one of imperfect foresight over very long contract periods. Decentralised clients thought that they lacked experience, capacity and time to write good OS (Chapter 3, Section 3.6).

(c) The vast majority (84%) of all respondents thought that a broadly appropriate allocation of risks had been achieved. A minority (22%) of private sector respondents thought that they had been required to bear too much risk. No one thought that too much risk was being borne by the client (Chapter 3, Section 3.7).

(d) Very few respondents (7%) thought their project was 'too small' to obtain value for money from PFI (Chapter 3, Section 3.8).

(e) A minority (20%) of respondents was, to some degree, critical of the suitability of PFI to their project. This criticism came equally from the public and private sectors (Chapter 3, Section 3.8).

(f) A significant proportion of public sector respondents felt that the VFM comparator used in their project had been constrained by affordability or feasibility limits. These were overwhelmingly decentralised clients.

(g) Respondents' organisations were focusing their activity to improve the performance of PFI on areas of standardisation of the award process and of contracts. Areas associated with technologically based innovation were cited relatively infrequently.

We conclude from these responses that while, taken as a whole, there is at least a moderate level of satisfaction with PFI processes, there are some areas of focused dissatisfaction in relation to OS among both decentralised public sector clients and private sector respondents that deserve further attention.

7.2 Recommendations

Most of the focus in the PFI literature to date has been on commercial (e.g. contract standardisation), political (e.g. public sector balance sheet treatment), financial (the actual impact of higher private sector borrowing costs) and organisational (e.g. role of the Treasury Taskforce) issues. This is understandable, but as a result issues related to the quality and cost of the operating service and design and construction of the underlying asset have been neglected. This study was intended to redress the balance, and it is important to maintain the momentum of attention to these issues that we hope its publication will generate. Specifically, the following issues need to be adressed.

(a) Steps are required to maximise the benefits of PFI experience gathered to date within the public sector, and to reduce the number of inexperienced public sector managers taking unsupported responsibility for procuring PFI projects.

(b) There is a case to consider for allowing more time at the ITN stage of bids in some instances to allow development of innovative proposals. Alternatively, bid evaluation criteria could be amended to recognise the positive contribution of innovative proposals.

(c) It may be unrealistic to expect equal amounts of cost saving innovation across all types of project. Some potentially promising areas could perhaps be identified, whether by expert panels or by market testing, and then prioritised in terms of bringing projects to the market.

(d) Because public sector PFI project expertise is a scarce resource, it may also make sense to concentrate this resource on types of project where best value review reveals the established public sector procurement and provision to be relatively less efficient.

(e) Further investigation is urgently needed to assess what actions or changes, if any, would significantly improve potential cost savings in those types of project and types of procuring entity where this study indicates results to date have been less impressive.

(f) There are, of course, strong reasons why the appropriate field of complete service PFIs may be limited. These will have to do mainly with issues of accountability, uncertainty, political choice, and difficulty of quality specification and monitoring for certain kinds of professional public service activity (Corry *et al.*, 1997) – issues outside the scope of this report. The balance between advantages from better VFM from complete service PFI projects and offsetting disadvantages will presumably vary between different types of project according to the specific strength of the problems created by these offsetting factors.

It seems that where a central client has formed a clear view about the general direction of desirable change in operating regime, 'complete service' PFI will be more successful at achieving cost savings than where this is not the case.

(g) We strongly concur with the following recommendation of the Andersen/LSE Report: 'We consider that there would be considerable value in local authorities, NHS trusts and other public sector bodies creating arrangements providing for the transfer or secondment within the public sector of staff with the appropriate skills and experience. We see considerable value in creating a group of professional public sector managers, possibly directly employed by the Office of Government Commerce, who as part of their career work on a series of projects'. (Recommendation 2.5)

(h) The benefits of experience are reinforced if embedded in a programme of similar projects, procured by the same agency. Insofar as there are project types for which VFM gains may outweigh losses of local accountability, some presently decentralised PFI projects could be more effectively procured more centrally. At present, it seems that rather similar projects are sometimes being procured in an unnecessarily fragmented way.

There appear to be areas where it is difficult at present to reconcile the objectives of VFM, local accountability of providers to the decentralised public sector client, and involvement in the PFI procurement process of the user entity. In this context, there is scope for a review to examine the respective roles and responsibilities of public sector clients (awarding authorities), procurement agents managing the PFI process on behalf of the clients, and client advisers.

Specialised public sector PFI procurement agencies (hypothetical organisations such as *English Schools PFI Procurement, West of England PFI Procurement*), procuring on behalf of decentralised clients, if created might be able to offer the latter VFM benefits more similar to those achieved by centralised clients. There would undoubtedly be a range of questions that would have to be resolved before such an arrangement could be made to work, but we believe the idea merits investigation.

(i) Further research would seem to be most urgently indicated to identify 'key' attributes of highly effective (and, indeed, of highly ineffective) OS.

(j) Following on from the research called for above (i), further guidance should be published to suggest how the procurement process can be improved in terms of asset and OS. TTF Technical Note No. 7, *How to achieve good design in PFI,* is a potentially valuable recent contribution along these lines.

Appendices

A.1 Methodology

The research project reported here comprised the following stages. The first consisted of preliminary activities, necessary to identify the principal sources of information, to set up the main headings of the problem, and to formulate the research questions. The second stage, and the longest, included the preparation of a database of project contact details, design of an appropriate research instrument, and the accomplishment of a survey of a large number of participants in PFI projects. Thirdly, the analysis of responses to the survey was carried out, looking, in particular, at three individual sectors of PFI projects and subsequently, developing case studies. Finally, the preparation of the final report completed the cycle of research. A brief description of the principal activities is shown in the following sections.

A.1.1 Stage 1: preliminary activities

Test enquiry and literature review

In order to set up the main headings of the problem, the two principal activities that were carried out were a review of the existing literature and a test enquiry. The literature review included policy statements, government guidance, available case studies, academic publications and other kinds of PFI-related publications, such as in the specialised press.

The test enquiry took the form of a series of lengthy interviews with key executives who had already participated in PFI projects. Public and private organisations were included in the exercise. Interviewees included: heads of (or senior executives in) PFI/PPP units of different public agencies; members of SPVs and of construction/operation companies; members of advising companies; and researchers in PFI procurement.

The outcome of this work was a definition of priorities, and the headings of the investigation, as well as the refinement of the central hypotheses originally considered for the project. The interviews were conducted in a semi-structured way, covering the main issues of the problem, the principal supporters and inhibitors of cost-saving innovation, the initial hypotheses of the research and any other matters arising.

A.1.2 Stage 2: survey

Database preparation

A questionnaire appropriate for use in a wide survey was developed and distributed throughout the PFI sector. It was decided that the respondents to the questionnaires would be at the project management level, rather than the strategic level, as had been the case with interviewees at the previous stage. The reason for this was the project-specific character of the questions that would be included in the survey instrument.

It was considered that the basic conditions for projects to be included in the sample were:

- to have already reached financial close (the moment of signing and commencement of the sets of contracts and agreements constituting a PFI deal)
- and to have an important content of construction-related services.

The reason for the former criterion was our desire, as far as possible, to elicit opinions based on, ideally, actual achievement of cost savings, or at least, terms agreed between the organisations participating in the PFI contract. Second, considering the scope of the research and the interests of its sponsors, it was appropriate and beneficial for the research to bound its scope to the construction-related projects.

Using these criteria, 122 projects were identified as potentially appropriate for inclusion in the survey. On each of these projects, we sought to survey the representatives on that project of: the public sector client; the client's principal advisers; the PFI company or special purpose vehicle (SPV); and the SPV's principal suppliers (of design, construction and operating services).

Even the most complete publicly or commercially available databases at that time did not include information on the full set of participants' project managers' or representatives' names and contact details. It was therefore necessary to collect this information, and a special purpose database was built, containing: descriptive information about each project, necessary for its inclusion and classification in the sample; and also the necessary information about the participant organisations and their representatives. The total number of organisations included in the database was over 600, and the final number of addressees to whom the questionnaire was sent was nearly 400 (many addresses receiving more than one questionnaire, because they had been responsible for more than one project).

Survey

The survey instrument was developed in a form designed to elicit, from a wide range of respondents and thus perspectives for each project, a view of actual results, perceptions and expectations. The respondents were asked to give their personal views of the facts as experienced professionals, rather than their organisations' official opinions. Different versions of the instrument had to be developed for each of the four types of respondent (clients, their advisers, SPVs and suppliers to SPVs). The instrument was piloted among a minor sample of the prospective respondents.

The survey was finally addressed to a total of 94 PFI projects out of the 122 initially identified. That is, 28 projects were excluded from the survey as not in fact meeting the criteria for inclusion or as lacking necessary contact information. At least one completed questionnaire was returned from 67 of those 94 projects

A.1.3 Stage 3: survey analysis and case studies

Stage 3 consisted of the analysis of the completed questionnaires returned in time. The statistical tools used for this study are fairly simple, known as 'small numbers' statistical methods. Although a small sample in statistical terms, it represents a unique effort of real statistical significance, considering its size relative to the whole population of PFI projects.

Additionally, and as a result of the preliminary analysis of responses to the survey, it was decided to incorporate a more detailed discussion about three particular sectors – the custodial sector, the healthcare sector and the highways sector. These three sectors, both separately and together, represent an important proportion of PFI activity, and represent a range of conditions and outcomes. They are also sectors for which we had a sufficient number of responses to permit separate analysis. To the respective responses to the survey we added the results of additional post-survey interviews and follow-ups. The results of this analysis are shown as a series of comparisons of each of the sectors with the general characteristics of the whole of PFI activity, represented by the complete survey.

Finally, two case studies were considered. The reasons why the case studies were developed and how they were selected are presented in the Introduction to Chapter 6.

A.2 Example of the questionnaires used in the survey

For the purposes of the study, a four-type set of questionnaires was designed. Each of those four types was addressed to one out of four different kinds of informants, as specified in A.1 (PFI clients, client advisers, SPVs and SPV suppliers).

The following pages include the main body of the questionnaire that was sent to the PFI clients (i.e. Questionnaire Type 1). It must be added that the survey also included:

- an introduction
- Part A, in which the completion or amendment of the details of the project were requested
- some explanatory notes about the concepts used in the questionnaire, and
- a cover letter addressing the survey.

It is also worth noting that in the questions that required an appraisal of the relevance of variables or the ranking of variables, the scales to do so were inverted in between the ones used in the questionnaires and the ones used to present the results in this text. This, of course, does not affect the validity of the conclusions finally drawn.

3. Savings obtained in each of the stages of the process

For each of the following stages of the project (at which the costs were / are expected to be incurred): how would you quantify the costs savings (-) or extra costs (+) obtained / expected in relation to the comparator set up for this purpose? (e.g. PSC or benchmark in the case of Public Sector and Competitors or Benchmarks in the case of a bidder). Please circle as appropriate.

Preliminary studies and detail design (design fees)

-20% or more	-20 to -10%	-10 to -5%	-5 to +5%	+5 to +10%	+10 to +20%	+20% or more

Other fees (including legal, due diligence, etc.)

-20% or more	-20 to -10%	-10 to -5%	-5 to +5%	+5 to +10%	+10 to +20%	+20% or more

Construction (Construction Contract(s) price)

-20% or more	-20 to -10%	-10 to -5%	-5 to +5%	+5 to +10%	+10 to +20%	+20% or more

Facilities management (FM fees)

-20% or more	-20 to -10%	-10 to -5%	-5 to +5%	+5 to +10%	+10 to +20%	+20% or more

Core operations of the facility (operation costs)

-20% or more	-20 to -10%	-10 to -5%	-5 to +5%	+5 to +10%	+10 to +20%	+20% or more

Total Contract Costs

-20% or more	-20 to -10%	-10 to -5%	-5 to +5%	+5 to +10%	+10 to +20%	+20% or more

4. Kinds of Cost Saving Innovations generated

In the following sections, several questions require a rank of the importance of a series of options. To do so, please write in the available space a number, starting from "1" for the most important item and finishing with r

a) Considering those CSI's generated and applied (or generated and expected to be applied) during this particular project: please rank the following ways in which CSI's may have been generated:

___ Generated as an incremental innovation to a current practice
___ Generated from prototype to application within the project
___ Generated as a reproduction of applications already existent in other industries
___ Generated as a reproduction of applications already existent in the construction industry outside the UK
___ Generated as a reproduction of applications already existent in the operating industry outside the UK

b) What is the proportion of CSI's which had (are expected to have) technological roots? (i.e. the principles originating them are technical)

Most of them	About a half of them	Some of them	None of them

Among the CSI's applying new technologies to the *Construction Process*:

Please rank the following disciplines, according to the relevance of the respective CSI's:

___ Soil Mechanics	___ Structural Engineering	___ Other (specify)
___ Architecture	___ IT	
___ Mechanical Engineering	___ Utilities Engineering	
___ Electrical Engineering	___ Transport Engineering	

Please rank the order of importance of the following technology areas:

___ Standardisation of components ___ New communication IT applications
___ Pre-fabrication of elements / New transport/assembly procedures ___ New design / manufacture / control IT applications
___ Utilisation of new materials / components ___ Utilisation of new exploratory/testing techniques
___ Utilisation of new construction equipment / machinery ___ Other (specify)

PART B1

1. Traditional Procurement of facilities OF THE SAME TYPE

This question refers to your experience in 'traditional' projects for this type of facility and where you think the greatest scope for re-thinking the process exists within the traditional procurement. Please rate the relative scope for improvement of each of the of the following categories:

For the sections 1 and 2, please tick as appropriate, according to the following categories:

1	2	3	4	5

1: Crucial   4: Of low relevance
2: Very relevant   5: Irrelevant
3: Relevant

Briefing Process

1	2	3	4	5

Design Process

1	2	3	4	5

Construction Process

1	2	3	4	5

Operating Process

1	2	3	4	5

Additional Revenue Opportunities (3rd Parties)

1	2	3	4	5

Procurement Arrangements / Bidding Process

1	2	3	4	5

2. Scope for cost saving innovations within THIS project

Compared to previous procurement of projects of the same type, including previous PFI projects, where do you believe there is most scope for innovation to reduce final costs of supply of service? Please, assess the relevance of each of the following elements.

Reducing excess of capacity

1	2	3	4	5

Reducing excess of durability

1	2	3	4	5

Reducing excess of risk protection

1	2	3	4	5

Accelerating the speed of the construction cycle

1	2	3	4	5

Improving the Buildability

1	2	3	4	5

Standardising components

1	2	3	4	5

Improving Quality Management (Cost of errors)

1	2	3	4	5

Improving the durability of the assets

1	2	3	4	5

Improving the Space Planning or functional suitability

1	2	3	4	5

Improving the staff efficiency during operation services

1	2	3	4	5

Improving other inputs' efficiencies during operation (e.g. energy)

1	2	3	4	5

Improving the mix of new build and refurbishment

1	2	3	4	5

Eliminating unnecessary non-functional design elements

1	2	3	4	5

Improving new technologies of construction or operations

1	2	3	4	5

Improving the procurement efficiencies

1	2	3	4	5

Other (specify) _____

1	2	3	4	5

d) The following is a list of possible participants involved in WRITING the OS of this project. Please rank the TWO most important in that process.

___ PFI / PPP Unit of the Department of State (Ministry)   ___ Advisers to the Awarding Authority
___ Managers of the Awarding Authority/Project Team   ___ Users of facilities similar to the one to be procured
___ Final Users   ___ Others (Specify) ___
___ Treasury Taskforce / 4 P's / PFPE

e) Following the Treasury Guidance terminology, would you say that the OS of this project were PRINCIPALLY of:

i.- Functional-type (i.e. defined the function to be performed)   iv.- A combination of i. and ii.
ii.- Performance-type (i.e. defined the performance required of its items)   v.- A combination of ii. and iii.
iii.- Technical-type (i.e. defined the technical and physical characteristics of its items)   vi.- A combination of i. and iii.

f) Was there a previously prepared design solution of the facilities when the project was tendered?
[ ] Yes [ ] No
If no, do you think that having one might have helped to make the bidding process...
□ Shorter? [ ]Yes [ ]No   □ Cheaper? [ ]Yes [ ]No
□ Easier? [ ]Yes [ ]No   □ More accountable? [ ]Yes [ ]No
□ Clearer? [ ]Yes [ ]No

g) Regarding any aspects of the use of the OS with which you were NOT completely satisfied or found particularly difficult to formulate, the following is a list of the possible sources of difficulty (illustrative examples are included). Please assess the relevance of each of them (tick as appropriate).

For the following questions, please tick as appropriate, according to the following categories:

| 1 | 2 | 3 | 4 | 5 |

1: Crucial   4: Of low relevance
2: Very relevant   5: Irrelevant
3: Relevant

□ The time period of the contract. E.g.:
- Facing long contracts, as in PFI, implies eventual future loss of flexibility
- The treatment of future disagreements within the OS requires extra elaboration

| 1 | 2 | 3 | 4 | 5 |

□ Complexity of the project. E.g.:
- The uncertainty and risks of the project force inclusion of contingency items
- The many details of the project made the simplification of the OS difficult

| 1 | 2 | 3 | 4 | 5 |

□ Excessive demands upon the Client's team. E.g.:
- Lack of in-house design skills implied a more difficult OS elaboration process
- Lack of historical data restrained the elaboration of the OS

| 1 | 2 | 3 | 4 | 5 |

□ Prior Experience in PFI. E.g.:
- Lack of a model for incorporating technical evaluation criteria in the OS
- A lack of templates for writing OS existed at that time

| 1 | 2 | 3 | 4 | 5 |

□ Legal & Technical Constraints. E.g.:
- Manuals, Codes, Norms, Standards, etc. restrained the elaboration of the OS.
- Intellectual Property issues restrained the elaboration of the OS

| 1 | 2 | 3 | 4 | 5 |

□ External approvals. E.g.:
- External approvals made the process slower and more difficult
- Activities of third parties delayed or restrained the process

| 1 | 2 | 3 | 4 | 5 |

Among CSI's applying new technologies to the *Operation Process*, please rank the order of importance of the following technology areas:

___ Utilisation of equipment instead of personnel
___ Utilisation of new equipment / machinery to replace existing
___ New transport / logistics systems
___ New monitoring techniques / procedures
___ Utilisation of new components / materials in maintenance
___ Others (specify) ___

c) The following are possible reasons why the CSI's generated in this project had NOT been applied to similar projects in the UK before. Please rank the importance of each of those reasons.

□ Before this project, the required technical expertise did not exist...
___ ...in your organisation
___ ...in the industry
___ ...in the country
___ ...at all

□ Until the date of this project, the contractual environment did not allow their application ...
___ ...because of technical codes, norms or similar
___ ...because the organisational way of doing things inhibited it
___ ...because the incentives to innovate were weak
___ ...because of contractual arrangements with third parties
___ ...because of veto / bargaining with 3rd parties

5. Proposals of CSI's that were ACCEPTED and (are being) IMPLEMENTED

a) Please briefly describe THE MOST SIGNIFICANT single CSI in this project (indicate the value of the saving if known) ___

b) Who proposed the CSI in 5a) originally? (please tick only one)

Client & its advisers [ ]   Operator [ ]   Other (specify) [ ]
SPV & its advisers [ ]   Sub-Contractor/Supplier [ ]
Principal contractor [ ]   Principal Designer [ ]

c) In which stage did the idea that generated the proposal in 5a) arise? (please tick only one)

Concept Design [ ]   Contract negotiation [ ]   On-site [ ]
Detail Design [ ]   Financing Negotiation [ ]   Other (specify) [ ]
Design Review [ ]   Construction Planning [ ]

PART C1A

1. - Output Specifications (OS)

a) What was the size of the OS documentation of the project? (Approx. no. of pages, incl. appendixes) ___

b) The size of the Facility Specification documentation? (Approx. no. of pages, incl. appendixes) ___

c) And the size of the Operation Specification documentation? (Approx. no. of pages, incl. appendixes) ___

b) How many other non-PFI projects of the same type (e.g. hospitals, offices, roads) had your organisation procured (participated in similar role if your organisation is an advising one), during the previous 5 years? _____

c) In organisational culture terms, what has PFI meant for your organisation?

[A radical change] [A large change] [A moderate change] [Little / none]

d) Regarding the factors that had most importance in that cultural change, please tick the TWO most relevant from the following list:

☐ Giving up responsibilities formerly borne by your organisation
☐ Procuring contracts / facilities / services of much larger size / value / cost
☐ Procuring contracts of more significant uncertainty / much greater duration
☐ Changing the way to deal with risks
☐ Working with new partners, forming new long-term Public-Private Partnerships
☐ Changing the emphasis from procurer/employer to monitor
☐ Improving the negotiation skills
☐ Other (specify) _____

5. - About Attitude to Risk

This question refers to the attitude towards risks taken as a whole, shown by each of the different participants in this project. Please assess the degree of ACCEPTANCE OF RISK shown by each of them according to a 1 to 5 scale (1= Very willing to accept risks, 5=Very reluctant to accept risks):

□ Client [1 2 3 4 5] □ Principal Contractor [1 2 3 4 5] □ Financiers [1 2 3 4 5]

□ SPV [1 2 3 4 5] □ Operator(s) [1 2 3 4 5] □ Sub-contractors/suppliers [1 2 3 4 5]

PART D

1. - About the Value For Money Comparator (VFMC)

a) What kind of VFMC or Reference Project (if previous guidance was followed) did the Full Business Case include? (please tick as many boxes as appropriate)

☐ i) A conventionally funded solution, providing a service of the same level (similar level) as the one considered in the Output Specifications
☐ ii) A conventionally funded solution, providing a service of a lower level than the one considered in the Output Specifications (e.g. "do minimum", "do nothing" or "do it much later")
☐ iii) A PFI solution based on the experience from previous PFI projects and adjusted to these particular Output Specifications
☐ iv) Other (specify) _____

b) In which of the following stages of the project did you develop the fundamental version of the VFMC/Ref. Project (when main elements were no longer modified)? (please tick one)

☐ Appraisal of options
☐ Outline Business Case
☐ Invitation for expression of interest – OJEC publication
☐ Prequalification of bidders
☐ Selection of Long-List
☐ Invitation to Negotiate
☐ BAFO & Selection of Preferred Bidder
☐ Full Business Case

c) Please rank (in order, from 1 to 5) the following groups of elements of risk, according to the impact they had on the risk adjustment carried out during the project appraisal.

—— Pre-Construction Risks
E.g.: Planning applications risk / Availability of site/delay in gaining site or existing facilities access

---

☐ Interfaces. E.g.:
– Due to existing-to-new-facilities compatibility, simple technical requirements had to be defined in a functional or performance way, making the OS writing a more difficult process. [1 2 3 4 5]

☐ Procurement restraints. E.g.:
– It was decided that existing drawings should not be used. [1 2 3 4 5]

2. - The particular attributes of the project

a) Bearing in mind the VFM objectives of PFI, in relation to the risks transferred to the Private Sector, please tick the most appropriate statement for this project:

☐ Risks that should have been transferred to the SPV are being borne by the Public Sector
☐ There was an adequate balance of risks transferred to the SPV and borne by the Public Sector
☐ Risks that should have been borne by the Public Sector were included in the PFI Contract
☐ There was an important excess of transference of risks from the Public sector to the SPV

b) Regarding the size (in value) of the project and its effects on the potential VFM obtainable, would you say that ...

☐ ...the project was too small?
☐ ...the project had an adequate size?
☐ ...the project was too large?
☐ ...the size of the project had nothing to do with its potential VFM?

c) In relation to this particular project: How suitable would you say that the PFI procurement model is? (tick as appropriate)

[Very Suitable] [Suitable] [Suitable with amendments] [Unsuitable]

3. - Experience, training and relations of the participant staff

a) Approximately HOW MANY people from your organisation participated in the project, at its maximum? (1= One full-time employee; please complete with figures)

Management / Professional Staff _____ Support Staff _____

b) Regarding the management / professional staff, please indicate HOW MANY people had previously participated in PFI projects, classifying them by level of experience.

Substantial Experience _____ Some Experience _____ None _____

c) Also regarding the management / professional staff, please indicate HOW MANY of them had previously participated in projects of the same type, procured by other routes than PFI, classifying them by level of experience.

Substantial Experience _____ Some Experience _____ None _____

d) HOW MANY of these professionals received formal training about PFI and its implications before or during the project? Please classify them by level of training.

Special & Complete Training _____ Some Training _____ None _____

e) How would you describe the work atmosphere of the team you worked in within your organisation during this particular project? (tick as appropriate)

[Very Good] [Good] [Moderately Poor] [Very Poor]

4. - Organisational experience/learning in PFI

a) How many PFI projects of the same type (e.g. schools, prisons, residential accommodation) had your organisation procured before this one? _____ ("Your organisation" as defined in the introduction).

- Construction Risks
  E.g.: Design change / Construction cost/time overruns / Equip. costs / IT costs / Inflation during construction
- Future Demand Risks
  E.g.: Traffic volume / Level of occupancy / Future number of patients or prisoners
- Performance and /or suitability of the service provided
  E.g.: Availability of the new facility / Availability of the service or its elements / Facility or equipment unsuitability/ Performance of the provided non-core services/FM / Client management & non-transferred Core Services/ Technology change/obsolescence
- Other Operation Risks
  E.g.: Life cycle/maintenance costs/service costs / Replacement costs / Latent defects on existing assets
- Other Risks
  E.g.: Contractors insolvency / Change of law / Partnership / Contractual risk / Statutory / Safety / Security risks / Third party action/protests / Industrial action / Other (specify)

d) Would you say that the chosen VFMC ... (tick one as appropriate)
☐ ...represents the option that might have offered the best VFM, if procured by the Public Sector?,
☐ ...represents the best VFM option within the existing affordability restraints?, or
☐ ...represents the only feasible alternative option for the Public Sector?

e) Would you say that the area of public service to which this project belongs is one in which...(Please tick only one)
☐ ...the client Department used to obtain efficient solutions before PFI?
☐ ...the client Department used to obtain moderately inefficient solutions before PFI?
☐ ...the client Department used to obtain highly inefficient solutions before PFI?

2. - About the Actual Results obtained

a) Please complete the following data, referring to the Business Case of the Project:
☐ Total NPV of the PSC:
☐ At the Final Business Case approval, Total NPV of the PFI solution: £
  - And (%) over the PSC: £
☐ At the selection of the preferred bidder, Total NPV of the PFI solution £
  - And (%) below the runner-up

b) Comments in respect to Part D

_____
_____
_____
_____
_____

PART H

1. - About the organisation's efforts in searching for Cost Savings

Which are the areas in which you are currently most actively working to make the PFI process more efficient and/or effective? (please tick AT MOST THREE)

- Standardisation of the PFI process
- Standardisation of the contracts used in PFI
- Standardisation of internal procedures
- Standardisation of products, construction elements or similar
- Formal training of staff
- Recruitment of specialists / new personnel to become specialists
- Development of new technologies
- Development of new products / services
- Development of new financial arrangements
- Formal examination of past experience (yours or others)
- Contractual arrangements between partners / value chain
- Others (specify)

2. - About the PFI industry's efforts

a) The list below includes the sources where the necessary savings might be generated in order to make PFI projects more effective and efficient. Please rank the FIVE MOST IMPORTANT according to their relevance to projects OF THIS TYPE

> This question requires ranking the importance of a series of options. To do so, please write in the available space a number, starting from "1" for the most important item and finishing with the largest

- Standardisation of the process
- Improvement of facilities' design
- Better equipment design / utilisation
- Improvements in the core-operation regime
- Improvement of construction techniques
- Lifting of legal/political restrictions
- Improvement of project finance
- Better management of public sector
- Better training of staff
- Improved relationships among contractual parties
- Re-focused scope of final service provided
- Improved relationships between the public sector client and the final user
- Other (specify)

b) General comments in relation to "PART H" and the whole Questionnaire

_____
_____
_____
_____
_____

Thank you very much.
Please post the completed questionnaire back in the pre-paid envelope provided. ☐
Please tick the box if you are not willing to be contacted by the research team. ☐

A.3 Survey size and scope

The respondents to the questionnaire were project managers of participant organisations on PFI projects. The survey was addressed to a total of 94 PFI projects. The basic conditions for a project to be included in the sample were to have already reached financial close ('signed'), and to have an important content of construction-related services.

A.3.1 The sample and the total population of PFI projects

The first step in the description of the survey is to characterise the sample that was taken into consideration. For that reason, and in order to put the sample in context, the following comparison is made.

The Treasury PFI Taskforce (TTF) database showed the 'universe' or total population of 'signed' PFI projects of all kinds, as at May 1999, to be 207 projects. The TTF's list of projects was examined and the total number of projects with an important construction component was identified as 122 – that is, approximately 60% of all 'signed' PFIs. We then checked each project's TTF classification carefully against data from other PFI industry sources. Despite the fact that the information required to make this classification into construction/non-construction content was in several cases incomplete and/or contradictory with other sources, we are confident that our estimate is both as accurate as possible and close to the 'true' number.

This estimated population of 122 construction-content PFI projects should be compared to the sample of 94 projects actually addressed as part of the survey. The research team contacted the known public sector clients for each of the 122 projects, seeking the identity or confirmation of the names of the public sector's advisers, of the PFI company (SPV) and of the latter's principal suppliers (operators, designers, contractors). SPVs were then contacted to provide names and contact details of their principal suppliers. A project was only included in our survey if a full or nearly full set of contact information was obtained. Some 28 projects could not be surveyed, mainly (21 cases) because of absence of contact data. The research team decided not to consider 7 projects because they were too old, too big, too unique or too recent. Thus the projects included in the survey represented 77% of the estimated total of construction based 'signed' PFI projects at the date of the survey – summer 1999. This is shown in Table A.1.

TTF database		Survey	
[A] Projects with important construction component	[B] Projects without an important construction component	[C] Projects to which the survey was addressed	[D] Projects with responses to survey
122	85	94	67
Total: 207 projects		77% of [A]	55% of [A]

Table A.1 The sample in context

Some 459 questionnaires were sent out to 364 participant individual project representatives (some had participated in more than one project) on these 94 projects, as shown in Table A.2. In all, 108 questionnaires were completed and returned. At least one completed questionnaire was returned from 71% of projects (67 projects), and 30% of the persons surveyed returned questionnaires. The overall response rate (questionnaires returned as a percentage of questionnaires sent out) was 24%.

Type of respondent	Number of addressees	Number of questionnaires sent	Number of questionnaires received	Rate of response over number of addressees: %	Rate of response over number of questionnaires: %
Clients	82	94	32	39	34
SPVs – PFI companies	67	84	23	34	27
Client advisers	56	82	14*	25	17
SPVs suppliers	159	199	39†	25	20
Total	364	459	108	30	24

Table A.2 Detail of responses, classified by type of respondent

* Client advisers:
technical advisers: 11
legal advisers: 3

† Suppliers to SPVs:
contractors: 10
operators: 3
principal designers: 9
technical advisers/subcontractors: 14
legal advisers: 3

A.3.2 Type of addressee

For the selected projects, four different types of project informants were identified and four variations of the questionnaire were developed – with several common sections. The informants were classified as:

- clients: project managers within the organisation of the awarding authority
- client advisers: project managers within organisations advising clients
- SPVs: project managers within special purpose vehicles or PFI companies
- SPV suppliers: project managers of organisations supplying some sort of service to the SPVs (e.g. contractors, designers, operators, subcontractors, advisers and others).

A.3.3 Rate of response in detail

The origin of the responses received is shown in the following tables. These tables demonstrate how balanced the set of responses is, and how representative the results of the collected information are. It is therefore necessary to highlight some aspects of the distribution of respondents, as follows.

Responses were received from 67 different projects. In respect of the kind of respondents, following the classification adopted for the purposes of the survey, the results are illustrated in Table A.2. It can be seen that the highest rates of response were obtained from clients and SPVs, who are logically the most interested organisations in the results of such a survey. The only category in which the rate of response did not reach the threshold of 20% was client advisers.

A normal rate of response for this kind of questionnaire is not usually higher than 20%. Additionally, two factors must be considered: the complexity of the questionnaire and the time-scale for response. It took about 40 minutes for the questionnaire to be completed, according to original estimates based on the pilot survey, and many of the respondents required even more time, due to the need to consult with colleagues to complete certain sections requiring hard detailed data about the project. Therefore the rates of response are significantly better than would normally be expected.

Note, however, the low number of responses from operators. Some SPVs are operator-led, and therefore responses from such SPVs can also give an operator's perspective. Nevertheless, this low response has restricted the analysis and interpretation of parts of the questionnaire.

The sample analysed in the research represents:

- a high proportion of all construction-content PFI projects in existence (67 projects out of 115)
- a satisfactory number of responses in total (108), but a low average number of responses per project in the sample (1.6), and thus very limited capability to use multiple responses to analyse specific projects as cases; this was inevitable given that the average number of questionnaires sent out per project was only 4.9 and that the decision whether or not to respond was independently made by each participant
- a broadly comparable number of responses from each of the public and private sector 'sides' of involvement in PFI (55 responses from clients and their advisers, and 53 responses from SPVs and their suppliers)
- a substantial proportion of public sector clients (39%) and private sector PFI companies (34%) with experience of at least one 'signed' project with a construction content.

In relation to the type of facility associated with the projects from which the responses came, Table A.3 shows that, in general, balanced rates of responses were also obtained. The only important exceptions are in the education and housing sectors. There, the number of responses does not allow us to form clear conclusions for these sectors. However, this limitation does not, of course, prevent the respective responses from contributing to the analysis of the total sample, or the analysis by categories, such as building versus civil engineering, or centralised versus decentralised clients, as explained in later sections of the report.

Type of facility	Number of projects	Number of questionnaires sent	Number of questionnaires received	Rate of response: %
Accommodation (non-housing)	10	82	16	20
Housing	12	28	5	18
Prisons and similar	8	51	16	31
Healthcare accommodation	24	136	31	23
Transport	17	71	20	28
Education	16	66	11	17
Utilities	9	25	9	36
Total	94	459	108	24

Table A.3 Detail of responses, classified by type of facility

Investment	Number of questionnaires sent	Number of questionnaires received	Rate of response: %
£0–£12m	125	26	21
£13–£42m	93	25	27
£43–£99m	132	29	22
£100+	109	28	26
Total	459	108	24

Table A.4 Detail of responses, classified by size of the projects

Type of respondent	Number of questionnaires sent	Number of questionnaires received	Rate of response: %
Centralised clients	187	54	29
Decentralised clients	272	54	20

Table A.5 *Detail of responses, classified by type of client responsible for the project*

Type of facility	Clients	SPVs	Client advisers	SPV suppliers
Accommodation (non-housing)	6/16 = 38%	6/15 = 40%	1/17 = 6%	3/34 = 9%
Housing	2/10 = 20%	0/5 = 0%	1/6 = 17%	2/7 = 29%
Prisons and similar	3/8 = 38%	2/8 = 25%	2/8 = 25%	9/27 = 33%
Healthcare	9/24 = 38%	5/22 = 23%	3/23 = 13%	14/67 = 21%
Transport	8/16 = 50%	5/16 = 31%	4/12 = 33%	3/27 = 11%
Education	1/12 = 8%	3/11 = 27%	2/10 = 20%	5/33 = 15%
Utilities	3/8 = 38%	2/7 = 29%	1/6 = 17%	3/4 = 75%
Total	32/94 = 34%	23/84 = 27%	14/82 = 17%	39/199 = 20%

Table A.6 *Rate of response by type of facility and respondent*

Type of respondent	Centralised clients (questionnaires sent and received)	Decentralised clients (questionnaires sent and received)
Clients	18/41 = 44%	14/53 = 26%
SPVs – Concess.	11/38 = 29%	12/44 = 27%
Client Advisers	7/35 = 20%	7/47 = 15%
Suppliers to SPVs	18/73 = 25%	21/126 = 17%
Total	54/187 = 29%	54/272 = 20%

Table A.7 *Rate of response classified into projects with centralised and decentralised clients*

Government department	Number of questionnaires sent	Number of questionnaires received	Rate of response: %
DfEE	45	6	13
Department of Health	115	25	22
DSS	18	3	17
DETR	68	23	34
DTI	5	1	20
FCO	3	2	67
Home Office	71	20	28
Inland Revenue	5	0	0
Local Authorities	28	5	18
MoD	23	4	17
Northern Ireland Office	2	2	100
Scottish Office	65	14	22
Welsh Office	11	3	27
Total	459	108	24

Table A.8 *Rate of response classified by government department responsible for the project*

It is also interesting to look at the results shown in Table A.4. This demonstrates that the sample is representative of the varying size of projects. The rates of response are very similar among the four quartiles of the size distribution of projects. This is significant, as important conclusions about these size groups are obtained.

In the same way, the rate of response for the two principal types of client – centralised and decentralised – is shown in Table A.5. In this case, the number of responses for each group is the same, although the rate of response for decentralised clients is lower. There are seen to be more projects with the latter type of client in the population of PFI projects.

Finally, Tables A.6, A.7 and A.8 show the rates of response to the survey in a more detailed form. In these cases, the type of facility, the government department, the public and private sector responses as well as the type of client in the PFI projects are considered for the analysis.

A.4 Projects with answers to the survey

Type of facility	Gov. Dept	Awarding authority (If different from Gov. Dept)	SPV	Project title	Capital costs: £m	Date of signature
A	DoH	Nottingham Health Authority	Mill Group-led Consortium	Upgrade Headquarters - Nottingham Health Authority	3	Nov-97
A	DSS	DSS	Trillium	PRIME (Private Sec.Resou.Init.for Manag.of Estate)	4,000	Dec-97
A	HO	Derbyshire Police	Peveril Securities / Boltercourt Ltd.	Ilkeston Section Police Station	3	Dec-97
A	DSS	Contributions Agency	Newcastle Estates Partnership	DSS Longbenton (Newcastle Estate)	150	Feb-98
A	FCO		Arteos	British Embassy - Berlin	25	Jun-98
A	DTI		Laser (Teddington II) Ltd	National Physical Laboratory-Teddington, Middlesex	300	Sep-98
A	HO	Greater Manchester Fire and Civil Defence Authority	PFF Stretford Ltd	Stretford Fire Station and Divisional HQ	3	Dec-98
A	LCD	Northern Ireland Court Service	Consul Services (NI) Ltd	New Court Complex - Belfast	25	Feb-99
A	HO	Derbyshire Police	HBG Derby SPV Ltd.	Derby Divisional HQ & City Section Station	24	Feb-99
A	DETR	London Underground / British Transport Police	AP Services (London) Ltd	Central London HQ & Station - Transport Police	50	Apr-99
A	MoD	Naval Recruitment and Training Agency (NRTA)	Flagship Training Ltd	Fire Fighting Training Units (FFTU)	35	Apr-99
E	SO	Falkirk College of Further & Higher Education	Stirling Centre for Further Education	Falkirk College	60	Sep-97
E	DfEE	Dorset County Council	Jarvis Colfox Ltd	Sir John Colfox School, Bridport, Dorset	12	Nov-97
E	DfEE	University College London	Cruciform Services Ltd	Cruciform Building	90	Jan-98
E	DfEE	Kingston upon Hull LEA	Sewell Group	New Primary School in Victoria Dock	3	Jul-98
E	SO	Falkirk Council	The Class 98 Ltd	Bundled Schools Project - Falkirk Council	73	Aug-98
E	DfEE	London Borough of Hillingdon	Jarvis (Barnhill) Ltd	Barnhill Community High School	20	Dec-98
E	LA	London Borough of Enfield	Laing Hyder plc	World's End Lane Secondary School	25	Feb-99
E	DETR	Lewisham LEA	Chartwells	Lewisham Schools Catering Centre	4	Mar-99
H	DoH	Northallerton Health Services NHS Trust	Primary Medical Properties	Richmond Community Hospital	3	Nov-97
H	DoH	Carlisle Hospitals NHS Trust	Health Management Carlisle Plc	Cumberland Infirmary - Carlisle	87	Nov-97
H	DoH	South Buckinghamshire NHS Trust	United Healthcare	Support Services - Wycombe Hospital	48	Dec-97
H	DoH	Norfolk and Norwich Healthcare NHS Trust	Octagon Healthcare	Norfolk & Norwich Hospital	214	Jan-98
H	DoH	South Devon Health Care NHS Trust	Sir Robert McAlpine Healthcare-led Consortium	Dawlish Community Hospital	3	Feb-98
H	WO	Glan Hafren NHS Trust	King & Co Financial Services Ltd-led consortium	Chepstow Community Hospital	9	Feb-98
H	DoH	North Durham Health Care NHS Trust	Consort Healthcare (Durham) Ltd.	New District General Hospital for North Durham	96	Mar-98
H	DoH	Oxfordshire Mental Healthcare NHS Trust	Community Healthcare Facilities (Oxford) Ltd	Mental Healthcare Facilities Oxfordshire	9	Jun-98
H	SO	Law Hospital NHS Trust	Summit Healthcare (Law) Ltd	New Law District Hospital, Motherwell, Lanarkshire	148	Jun-98
H	DoH	Greenwich Healthcare NHS Trust	Meridian Hospital Company Plc	New Queen Elizabeth Hospital	85	Jul-98
H	DoH	Calderdale Healthcare NHS Trust	Catalyst Healthcare (Halifax) Plc	New Halifax General Hospital	77	Jul-98
H	SO	Royal Infirmary of Edinburgh NHS Trust	Consort Healthcare (Edinburgh Royal Infirmary) Ltd.	Royal Infirmary of Edinburgh & Univ Medical School	200	Aug-98
H	DoH	South Manchester University Hospitals NHS Trust	South Manchester Healthcare Ltd (SMHL)	Wythenshawe Hospital	66	Aug-98
H	DoH	Bromley Hospitals NHS Trust	United Healthcare	New Bromley Hospital	120	Nov-98
H	DoH	Oxleas NHS Trust	Ryhurst (Bexley) Ltd	Bexley Hospital	14	Dec-98
H	DoH	Wellhouse NHS Trust	Metier Healthcare Ltd	Barnet General Hospital	64	Feb-99
H	SO	Ayrshire & Arran Community Healthcare NHS Trust	HBG Cumnock SPV Ltd.	East Ayrshire Community Hospital (Cumnock)	9	Mar-99
H	DoH	Hereford Hospitals NHS Trust	Mercia Healthcare	Hereford District General Hospital	65	Apr-99
H	DoH	Newham Community Health Services NHS Trust	Grosvenor House Group Plc	New Healthcare Facilities - Newham	12	Aug-99
C	HO	HM Prison Service	Prison and Court Services Ltd	HMP Altcourse, Fazakerley, Merseyside	67	Dec-95
C	HO	HM Prison Service	Bridgend Custodial Services Ltd	HMP Parc, Bridgend, South Wales	43	Jan-96
C	HO	HM Prison Service	Lowdham Grange Prison Services	Lowdham Grange Prison - Nottinghamshire	37	Nov-96
C	SO	Scottish Prison Service	Premier Prison Services Ltd	Kilmarnock Prison	32	Nov-97
C	HO	HM Prison Service	Agecroft Prison Management Ltd	Forest Bank Prison-Agecroft, Salford, Gt Manchester	55	Jun-98
C	HO	HM Prison Service	Pucklechurch Custodial Services	Pucklechurch Prison, Ayrshire, Bristol	32	Jun-98
R	LA	Surrey County Council	Anchor Trust	Refurbishment of Residential Homes - Surrey	29	Mar-98
R	LA	North East Derbyshire District Council	South Yorkshire Housing Association	Social Housing - North East Derbyshire	2	Aug-98
R	MoD	Defence Housing Executive (DHE)	Western Challenge Housing Association	Married Quarters, Ilchester - Yeovilton	8	Sep-98
R	MoD	RAF	Riverside Housing Association	Married Quarters, RAF - Cosford / Shawbury	15	Mar-99
T	DETR	West Midlands PTE (Centro)	Travel Midland Metro	Midland Metro Line One	145	Aug-95
T	DETR	London Transport (LT)	Tramtrack Croydon Ltd	Croydon Tramlink	210	Nov-96
T	DETR	Greater Manchester Passenger Transport Executive	Altram (Manchester) Ltd	Manchester Metrolink - Salford Quays to Eccles.	126	May-97
T	SO	Highlands and Islands Airports Ltd (HIAL)	Inverness Air Terminal Ltd.	Inverness Airport Redevelopment	9	Apr-98
TR	DETR	Highways Agency	Road Link (A69) Ltd.	A69 Carlisle to Newcastle	24	Jan-96
TR	DETR	Highways Agency	Road Management Services (Peterborough) Ltd.	A1(M) Alconbury to Peterborough	128	Feb-96
TR	DETR	Highways Agency	Road Management Services (Gloucester) Ltd.	A419/A417 Swindon to Gloucester	100	Feb-96
TR	DETR	Highways Agency	Yorkshire Link Ltd.	M1-A1 (Yorkshire) Link	214	Mar-96
TR	DETR	Highways Agency	Connect A50 Ltd.	A50 Stoke to Derby Link	21	May-96
TR	DETR	Highways Agency	Connect A30 Ltd.	A30/A35 Exeter to Bere Regis	75	Jul-96
TR	DETR	Highways Agency	UK Highways Ltd.	M40 junctions 1-15	37	Sep-96
TR	DETR	Highways Agency	Autolink Concessionaires Ltd.	A19 Dishforth to Tyne Tunnel	29	Oct-96
TR	SO		Autolink Concessionaires (M6) Plc	A74(M) / M74 Upgrade (M6)	158	Dec-96
U	SO	Dundee City Council	Dundee Energy Recycling Ltd.	Baldovie Waste to Energy Plant	42	Sep-97
U	MoD	RAF	Thames Water	RAF Tidworth Water & Sewerage	10	Feb-98
U	DETR	London Underground Ltd	Seaboard Powerlink (SPL)	London Underground Power Supply	100	Aug-98
U	HO	HM Prison Service	Powerline Energy Services Ltd.	Prison Service New Energy Systems	9	Nov-98
U	LA	Worcester County Council & Hereford District Council	Mercia Waste Management Ltd.	Waste Management - Hereford & Worcester	75	Dec-98
U	SO	East of Scotland Water	Stirling Water	Almond Valley & Seafiled / Esk Valley	120	Mar-99

A : Accommodation (non-housing)
E : Education
H : Healthcare
C : Custodial
R : Residential
T : Transport - other than roads
TR : Transport - Roads
U : Utilities

Table A.9 *List of projects included in the survey*

A.5 Types of analysis of responses

In Chapters 3 and 4, a thorough analysis of the responses received for each area of the questionnaires is presented. The analysis in these chapters includes the results of the whole sample, and comparisons between different groups constituting the whole sample.

The analyses presented are basically of two types. The first one is the direct presentation of the distribution of answers to specific questions. In each of these cases comments are made, within a common framework. The second type of result is presented as analyses of difference and/or variance between different groups constituting the whole sample. In these cases, a series of comparisons are presented and discussed within the same framework.

A.5.1 Distribution of answers to specific questions

The questionnaire contained four different types of question that are presented in the following sections. They were questions of relevance of variables, ranking of variables, selection of variables from a set of options and open questions.

- Relevance of variables. The answers to these questions are presented according to the 'average relevance' of the variable included in each question. For that purpose, a scale of six points was used, according to the following definitions:
  0. the variable was reported as not even considered. It must be interpreted as 'not applicable'
  1. the variable is considered as 'irrelevant'
  2. the variable is considered as 'of low relevance'
  3. the variable is considered as 'relevant'
  4. the variable is considered as 'very relevant
  5. the variable is considered as 'crucial'.
- Ranking of variables. The answers to these questions are presented according to the explicit ranking by respondents of the set of variables included in the question. The results are presented in a scale from 0 to 5 (from least important to most important, respectively). We describe these relative rankings as 'relative importance'. Methodologically the difference from the analysis of 'relevance of variables' is that in this case scores are explicitly in relative order of importance only with one another and are mutually exclusive whereas, in the former, scores are derived by the respondent assessing importance as compared with an (implicit) benchmark, and are not mutually exclusive.
- Selection from a set of variables. The answers to these questions are presented according to the 'frequency' of response for each of the included variables. In these cases the respondent had to pick up to a certain maximum number of options from a given set of variables.
- Open questions. The answers to these questions are presented by 'frequency' of types of answer. The classification, in these cases, was made ex-post, according to the popularity of those types.

A.5.2 Analysis of difference between groups

In some cases, a secondary analysis of responses is made. It consists of the analysis of difference of relevance, relative importance or frequency, between different groups of respondents.

The typical secondary analyses of variance of response explored the possible effects on responses of one of the following structures of classification of projects or respondents.

- Analysis by type of facility. In this case, the projects are grouped by the type of facility associated with each of them. The categories used are:
  - accommodation (non-housing)
  - education
  - healthcare
  - custodial
  - housing
  - transport
  - utilities.

  However, these classes are sometimes grouped only in two categories: 'building' and 'civil engineering'. The latter is deemed to comprise 'utilities' and 'transport', and the former to comprise the remainder. The combining of groups into 'building' and 'civil engineering' had the beneficial effect of increasing the number in each category, and thus the statistical confidence with which significance could be attributed to observed difference.

- Analysis by type of client. In this case the projects are grouped in two sets. The first are projects in which the client – awarding authority – is a centralised agency of the government with substantial previous experience of procurement of similar facilities, although not necessarily of similar PFI services. These we called 'centralised clients'. The clients for the projects in the second group do not meet the above conditions and are classified as 'decentralised clients'. The most important centralised clients in our sample (those with most sample projects) were the Highways Agency, the Prison Service and the Ministry of Defence.

- Analysis by size of the project: In this case, the level of capital costs of the project is used to define what was called 'size'. The projects are subsequently grouped in four quartiles:
  - 1st quartile: projects with capital investment of up to £12m
  - 2nd quartile: projects with capital investment between £13m and £42m
  - 3rd quartile: projects with capital investment between £43m and £99m
  - 4th quartile: projects with capital investment of £100m or more.

- Analysis by scope of service provision. In this case, the projects are also grouped in two sets. The first are projects in which the PFI contract includes the provision of a complete service. In other words, the core operations of the public service are in the hands of the SPV or PFI company. An example of this is the DCMF prisons contracts granted by HM Prison Service, in which the SPV is responsible for the provision of the custodial services. This first group is labelled 'complete service' projects. The members of the second group do not meet the conditions and are classified as 'partial service' projects. A typical example of these cases is the usual PFI hospital project, in which the SPV is responsible for ancillary services, such as 'hard' and 'soft' facility management (FM), but in which the clinical services remain provided by the NHS Trust.

A.6 Reported cost savings – by type of facility

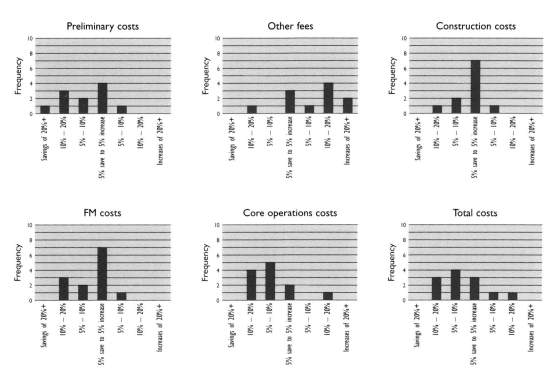

Figure A.1 *Reported cost savings – Accomodation non-housing*

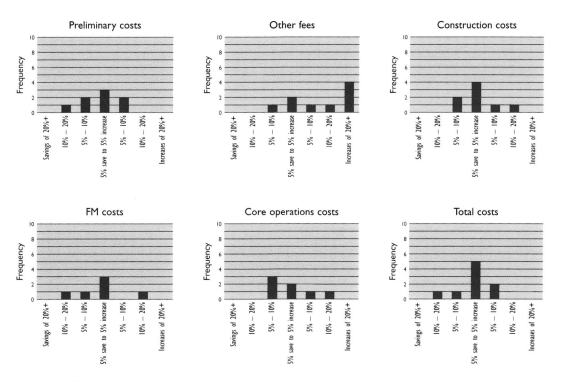

Figure A.2 *Reported cost savings – Education*

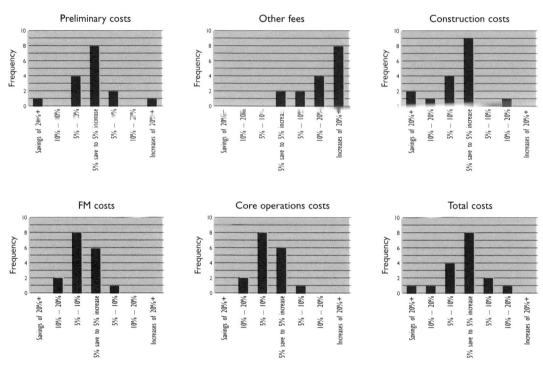

Figure A.3 *Reported cost savings – Healthcare*

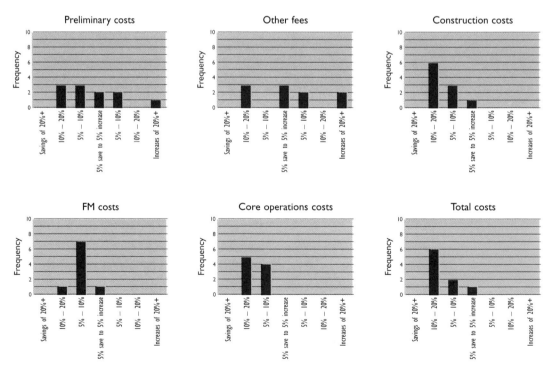

Figure A.4 *Reported cost savings – Custodial*

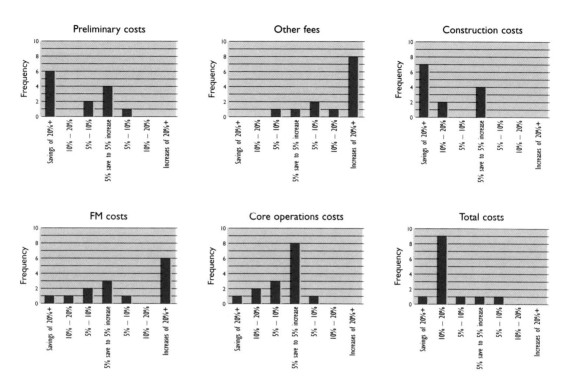

Figure A.5 *Reported cost savings – Transport (including highways)*

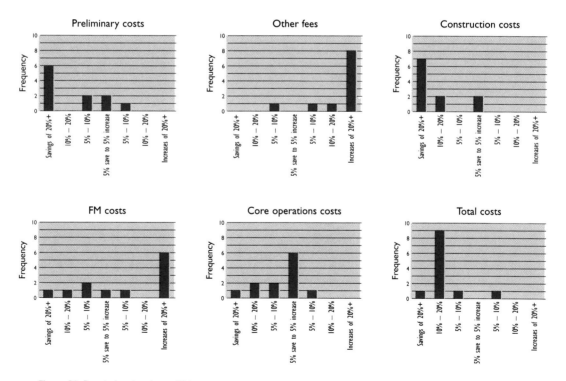

Figure A6 *Reported cost savings – Highways*

A.7 Chi-squared analysis

The analyses of variance applied in the research were carried out following the guidance on chi-squared analysis provided in texts such as Rowentree (1981) and Greenwood and Nikulin (1996). This was considered the most appropriate statistical significance test for the purposes of the study, both because of its fitness of purpose and its simplicity. It is worth considering, that such authors regard this test as useful, but incomplete if used by itself. It is suggested that joint use be made of it with another evaluation tool. In the case of the research, the graphical analysis, the qualitative interpretation of results and the multiple use of chi-squared testing were regarded as appropriate.

With regard to the interpretation given to the results obtained from the chi-squared tests, the following considerations were taken into account. Cases with figures under 1% attained a strong statistical significance, as they are interpreted as 99% of confidence. Cases with figures between 1% and 10% were considered as demonstrating some statistical tendency. Finally, cases with figures over 10% were considered as non-statistically significant.

TOTAL COST SAVINGS ESTIMATED BY DIFFERENT TYPE OF CLIENTS

OBSERVED

	Centralise	Decentralised			Oij-Eij		(Oij-Eij)^2/Eij	
-20% +	2	1	3		0.412	-0.412	0.107	0.120
-10% to -20%	18	3	21		6.882	-6.882	4.261	4.793
-5% to -10%	10	6	16		1.529	-1.529	0.276	0.311
+5% to -5%	4	16	20		-6.588	6.588	4.099	4.612
+10% to +5%	1	5	6		-2.176	2.176	1.491	1.678
+20% to +10%	1	1	2		-0.059	0.059	0.003	0.004
+20% +	0	0	0					
	36	32	68					
			68					

EXPECTED

	Centralise	Decentralised				
-20% +	1.59	1.41	3	Chi^2 = Sum[(Oij-Eij)^2/Eij]	21.754
-10% to -20%	11.12	9.88	21	df	5
-5% to -10%	8.47	7.53	16	CHITEST	0.058%
+5% to -5%	10.59	9.41	20		
+10% to +5%	3.18	2.82	6		
+20% to +10%	1.06	0.94	2		
+20% +	0.00	0.00	0		
	36	32	68		
			68		

OBSERVED

	Centralise	Decentralised			Oij-Eij		(Oij-Eij)^2/Eij	
-10%+	20	4	24		7.29	-7.29	4.19	4.71
-5% to -10%	10	6	16		1.53	-1.53	0.28	0.31
+5% to -5%	4	16	20		-6.59	6.59	4.10	4.61
+5%+	2	6	8		-2.24	2.24	1.18	1.33
	36	32	68					

EXPECTED

	Centralise	Decentralised			
-10%+	12.71	11.29		Chi^2 = Sum[(Oij-Eij)^2/Eij]	20.70
-5% to -10%	8.47	7.53		df	3
+5% to -5%	10.59	9.41		CHITEST	0.012134%
+5%+	4.24	3.76			
			68		

OBSERVED

	Centralise	Decentralised			Oij-Eij		(Oij-Eij)^2/Eij	
-5% +	30	10	40		8.82	-8.82	3.68	4.14
-5% -	6	22	28		-8.82	8.82	5.25	5.91
	36	32	68					

EXPECTED

	Centralise	Decentralised			
-5% +	21.18	18.82		Chi^2 = Sum[(Oij-Eij)^2/Eij]	18.97
-5% -	14.82	13.18		df	1
				CHITEST	0.001326%
			68		

Figure A.7 *Example of Chi-squared analysis for case illustrated in fig. 4.1*

A.8 Details of analysis of factors affecting the extent of cost savings

Range of cost savings (cost increases)	Total costs		Construction costs		FM costs		Core operation costs	
	C	D	C	D	C	D	C	D
Savings of 20% or more	2	1	7	2	1	0	2	0
Savings of 10–20%	18	3	10	1	4	4	10	4
Savings of 5–10%	10	6	8	8	12	10	14	11
5% savings to 5% increases	4	16	8	17	7	13	7	13
Increases of 5–10%	1	5	3	1	2	1	1	2
Increases of 10–20%	1	1	0	2	0	1	1	1
Increases of 20% or more	0	0	0	0	7	0	0	0
Total	36	32	36	31	33	29	35	31

Table A.10 *Relationship between cost savings in programme of projects and one-off projects*

C: centralised clients; D: decentralised clients

Range of cost savings (cost increases)	Total costs		Construction costs		FM costs		Core operation costs	
	C	B	C	B	C	B	C	B
Savings of 20% or more	2	1	7	2	1	0	2	0
Savings of 10–20%	10	11	3	8	1	7	3	11
Savings of 5–10%	4	12	3	13	3	19	5	20
5% savings to 5% increases	2	18	4	21	3	17	9	11
Increases of 5–10%	1	5	1	3	1	2	1	2
Increases of 10–20%	0	2	0	2	0	1	0	2
Increases of 20% or more	0	0	0	0	7	0	0	0
Total	19	49	18	49	16	46	20	46

Table A.11 *Relationship between cost savings in civil engineering and building projects*

C: civil engineering; B: building

Range of cost savings (cost increases)	Total costs		Construction costs		FM costs		Core operation costs	
	C+C	B-C	C+C	B-C	C+C	B-C	C+C	B-C
Savings of 20% or more	2	1	7	2	1	0	2	0
Savings of 10–20%	16	5	9	2	2	6	8	6
Savings of 5–10%	6	10	6	10	10	12	9	16
5% savings to 5% increases	3	17	5	20	4	16	9	11
Increases of 5–10%	1	5	1	3	1	2	1	2
Increases of 10–20%	0	2	0	2	0	1	0	2
Increases of 20% or more	0	0	0	0	7	0	0	0
Total	28	40	28	39	25	37	29	37

Table A.12 *Relationship between cost savings in civil engineering plus custodial and building projects (non-custodial)*

C+C: civil engineering plus custodial; B-C: building (non-custodial)

Range of cost savings (cost increases)	Total costs				Construction costs				FM costs				Core operation costs			
	Q1	Q2	Q3	Q4	Q1	Q2	Q3	Q4	Q1	Q2	Q3	Q4	Q1	Q2	Q3	Q4
Save 20%+	2	0	0	1	1	3	1	4	0	1	0	0	0	1	0	1
Save 10–20%	2	1	6	6	2	4	4	1	3	1	2	2	4	2	6	2
Save 5–10%	4	4	5	3	2	4	7	3	4	4	9	5	5	4	7	9
5% savings to 5% increases	8	5	3	4	9	6	5	5	7	4	4	5	7	6	2	5
Increase 5–10%	2	1	2	1	1	1	0	2	0	2	1	0	1	1	1	0
Increase 10–20%	0	1	1	0	1	0	1	0	1	0	0	0	0	2	0	0
Increase 20%+	0	0	0	0	0	0	0	0	1	3	0	3	0	0	0	0
Total	18	18	17	15	16	18	18	15	16	15	16	15	17	16	16	17

Table A.13 Relationship between cost savings in projects of different sizes

Q1: £0m–£12m; Q2: £13m–£42m; Q3: £43m–£99m; Q4: £100m+

Range of cost savings (cost increases)	Total costs		Construction costs		FM costs		Core operation costs	
	C	P	C	P	C	P	C	P
Savings of 20% or more	2	1	7	2	1	0	2	0
Savings of 10–20%	17	4	10	1	2	6	8	6
Savings of 5–10%	7	9	8	8	11	11	10	15
5% savings to 5% increases	5	15	5	20	4	16	10	10
Increases of 5–10%	1	5	2	2	1	2	1	2
Increases of 10–20%	0	2	0	2	0	1	0	2
Increases of 20% or more	0	0	0	0	7	0	0	0
Total	32	36	32	35	26	36	31	35

Table A.14 Relationship between cost savings in projects that include a complete service provision and a partial service provision

C: provision of a complete service;
P: provision of a partial service

Range of cost savings (cost increases)	Total costs		Construction costs		FM costs		Core operation costs	
	P	N	P	N	P	N	P	N
Savings of 20% or more	1	2	6	2	1	0	2	0
Savings of 10–20%	18	3	8	3	4	3	11	3
Savings of 5–10%	11	5	11	4	13	8	16	8
5% savings to 5% increases	12	3	18	4	16	2	16	2
Increases of 5–10%	6	0	3	0	2	0	2	0
Increases of 10–20%	1	0	1	0	1	0	1	0
Increases of 20% or more	0	0	0	0	7	0	0	0
Total	49	13	47	13	44	13	48	13

Table A.15 Relationship between cost savings in projects with performance-based OS and non-performance-based OS

P: performance-based OS;
N: non-performance-based OS

Range of cost savings (cost increases)	Total costs		Construction costs		FM costs		Core operation costs	
	T	N	T	N	T	N	T	N
Savings of 20% or more	1	2	1	7	1	0	1	1
Savings of 10–20%	4	17	3	8	3	5	4	10
Savings of 5–10%	5	11	2	13	5	15	6	18
5% savings to 5% increases	2	13	7	15	2	16	1	17
Increases of 5–10%	1	5	0	3	1	1	1	1
Increases of 10–20%	0	1	0	1	0	1	0	1
Increases of 20% or more	0	0	0	0	1	6	0	0
Total	13	49	13	47	13	44	13	48

Table A.16 Relationship between cost savings in projects with technically based OS and non-technically based OS

T: Technically based OS;
N: Non-technically based OS

Range of cost savings (cost increases)	Total costs		Construction costs		FM costs		Core operation costs	
	Y	N	Y	N	Y	N	Y	N
Savings of 20% or more	2	1	7	1	1	0	1	1
Savings of 10–20%	11	10	5	6	3	5	6	8
Savings of 5–10%	8	8	5	11	6	15	9	15
5% savings to 5% increases	8	11	11	14	7	13	11	9
Increases of 5–10%	2	4	1	3	2	1	1	2
Increases of 10–20%	1	1	0	2	0	1	1	1
Increases of 20% or more	0	0	0	0	7	0	0	0
Total	32	35	29	37	26	35	29	36

Table A.17 Relationship between cost savings in projects with and without a preliminary design provided by the public sector client

Y: preliminary design was provided at the bidding stage;
N: no preliminary design was provided at the bidding stage

A.9 Room datasheets – Stretford Fire Station

Figures A.2 and A.3 illustrate an example of the room datasheets in the PFI contract for the Stretford Fire Station.

Notes Room 41

TECHNICAL DESIGN DATA SHEET 41 A

ENVIRONMENTAL	PREF. REQUIR.	NOTES
AIR		
Winter Temperature (°)	18.5 C / 16 C	
Summer Temperature (°)	N/A	
Ventilation	Extract	
LIGHTING		
Service Illumination (Lux)	300-500 Lux	Work Area
Turn Out Lighting (Lux)	Yes	
Service Illumination – Night	None	
Emergency Lighting – Battery	Yes	
Emergency Lighting – Generator	None	
Visual Turn out Indicator	No	
NOISE		
Acceptable Noise Level Within	NR45	
Acceptable Noise Level Without	N/A	
Turn Out System	Yes	
Tannoy System	Yes	
SAFETY		
Accessible Hot Surface: Max. Temp (°)	60 C stored	
Domestic Hot Water Max. Temp. (°)	45 C at outlet	
ELECT / IT / COMM / FIN		
13 Amp sockets	Yes (Waterproof)	Extractor fa■
IT Outlets	No	
Telephone Outlet	No	
Fire Alarm	Yes	

DESIGN CHARACTERISTICS

INTERNAL FINISHES	WALLS	FLOOR	CEILING
Grade	Washable	Quarry tile	Acoustic
Doorsets	Secure digital lock to external door		
Windows	None		
Internal Glazing	No		
Hatch	No		
Notes	None		

GREATER MANCHESTER FIRE AND CIVIL DEFENCE AUTHORITY
PFI STRETFORD FIRE STATION AND 'A' DIVISION HEADQUARTERS

ACTIVITY DATA SHEET

ISSUE NO: 2 | **DATE: 27 July 1998**
ACTIVITY NAME: Equipment Cleaning / Maintenance Room
ROOM NO.: 41 & 45

ROOM CONTENTS

Low Level S/S sink double bowl and drainer
Worksurfaces, stainless steel or similar to resist damage
Vice-1 large HD type
Industrial cupboards under work tops
Sink Areas to have a ss splash back and above worktops
Industrial towel machine

NOTES

DESIGN REQUIREMENTS

Facilities needed for the following activities

The cleaning of soiled equipment and storage of hoses used with Fire Appliances

Personnel

Normally 2/3 personnel working on equipment

Additional Equipment & Engineering Outlets

Floor to be a 'Wet Area', scrubable floors with gulley with trap maintained via sink waste

Room Relationships

Direct Access to: Appliance room and Drill Yard
Ease Access to:
Close to: Drying Room

Figures A.8 and A.9 *Examples of room datasheet*

References

- CIC [1998]. *Constructors' key guide to PFI*, Thomas Telford, London.
- Corry, D. et al. (for the Institute of Public Policy Research) [1997]. *Public/private partnerships: a marriage of convenience or a permanent commitment?*, IPPR, London.
- Department of Transport [1993]. *Paying for better motorways* (Green Paper).
- Department of Transport [1994]. *Design, build, finance and operate concessions for trunk roads and motorways* (Green Paper).
- DETR [1998]. *Rethinking construction*, 'The Egan Report', DETR, London.
- Freeman, C. [1989]. *The economics of industrial innovation*, MIT Press, Cambridge, Mass., USA.
- Gaffney, D. and Pollock, A. [1999]. Pump-priming the PFI: why are privately financed hospitals schemes being subsidized?, *Public Money & Management*, Jan.–Mar., pp. 55–62.
- Greenwood, P.E. and Nikulin, M.S. [1996]. *A guide to chi-squared testing*, John Wiley & Sons, New York.
- HM Treasury [1991]. CUP Guidance No. 30: *Specification writing*, HM Treasury, London.
- HM Treasury Private Finance Taskforce [1998]. *Policy Statement No. 2: Public Sector Comparators and Value for Money*, HM Treasury, London.
- HM Treasury Private Finance Taskforce [2000]. *Value for Money Drivers in the Private Finance Initiative* (A Report by Arthur Andersen and Enterprise LSE), HM Treasury, London.
- HM Treasury Private Finance Taskforce [2000a]. *Technical Note No. 7: How to achieve good design in PFI*, HM Treasury, London.
- Hillebrandt, P.M. [1985]. *Economic theory and the construction industry*, MacMillan, London.
- Laborde, M. and Sanvido, V. [1994]. Introducing new process technologies into construction companies, *Journal of Construction Engineering and Management*, Vol. 120, No. 3, pp. 488–509.
- Munford, M. [1998]. *Public projects private finance: understanding the principles of the Private Finance Initiative*, NPV+ Griffin Multimedia, Welwyn Garden City.
- National Audit Office (NAO) [1994]. *Control of prison building projects*, HMSO, London.
- NAO [1997]. *The PFI contracts for Bridgend and Fazakerley prisons*, HM Prison Service, HMSO, London.
- NAO [1997a]. *The Skye Bridge*, The Scottish Development Department, HMSO, London.
- NAO [1998]. *The Private Finance Initiative: the first four design, build, finance and operate road contracts*, DETR, HMSO, London.
- NAO [1999]. *The Private Finance Initiative: the contract to complete and operate the A74(M)/M74 motorway in Scotland*, The Scottish Office Development Department, HMSO, London.
- NAO [1999a]. *The PRIME project: The transfer of the Department of Social Security estate to the private sector*, Department of Social Security, HMSO, London.
- NAO [1999b]. *The PFI contract for the new Dartford and Gravesham Hospital*, HMSO, London.
- NAO [1999c]. *Examining the value for money of deals under the Private Finance Initiative*, HMSO, London.
- PFI Report [1999]. *'The PFI Awards 1999'* (A Report on the Winners and Finalists – Category: Health), PFI Report, London.
- Private Finance Initiative Journal [1998]. *'Greenwich Quick Time'*, Vol. 3, Issue 4, pp. 44–48, Public Sector Information Ltd, Stockport.
- Private Finance Initiative Journal [1999]. *'Stretford Fire Station'*, Vol. 4, Issue 1, pp. 48–52, Public Sector Information Ltd, Stockport.
- Private Finance Panel Executive [1996]. *Writing an output specification*, HM Treasury, London.
- Rogers, E. M. [1983]. *Diffusion of innovations*, 3rd ed., MacMillan, New York.
- Rowntree, D. [1981]. *Statistics without tears*, Penguin, London.
- Slaughter, E.S. [1998]. Models for construction innovation, *Journal of Construction Engineering and Management*, Vol. 124, No. 3, pp. 226–231.
- UNISON [1999]. *Downsizing for the 21st Century* (A Report on the North Durham Acute Hospitals PFI Scheme, by Declan Gaffney and Allison Pollock), UNISON, London.
- Williamson, O. [1985]. *The economic institutions of capitalism*, Free Press, New York.

Constructors' key guide to PFI

Construction Industry Council

'I am encouraged to see the industry responding to the needs of its members. The guide emphasises the importance of the relationships between designers, constructors, financiers and service operators. This, in turn, should lead to the development of strong partnerships within the public sector to help renew the country's infrastructure for the 21st Century.'

Nick Raynsford MP

Department of the Environment, Transport and the Regions.

The Private Finance Initiative is an evolving form of procurement and is now a vital part of the Government's programme. It is a new way of working for companies involved in providing public services. All companies intending to seek construction work in the public sector must be aware of how PFI operates and find out how they can benefit from it.

The *Constructors' key guide to PFI* is the first published guide that provides a practical, straightforward explanation of PFI and fully describes the entire process of how to obtain construction work in the public sector. It specifically describes the different opportunities PFI presents to different types of company and how construction companies need to find new ways to work with a wide range of consultants and specialist service providers. This valuable guide explains the different roles in which constructors, be they consultants, builders or designers, can be involved in public sector work, and particularly highlights the opportunities that exist for smaller companies looking for sub-contract roles in PFI projects.

Aimed at those construction contractors and consultants that do not have an expert knowledge of the complexities of PFI but are big enough to be affected by it, the guide answers some of the questions and concerns in the industry and unravels the current complexities of PFI, to enable more constructors to understand the risk so that they can better capture the rewards.

Constructors' key guide to PFI shows you how to take advantage of the new challenges and great opportunities that PFI offers.

Contents

What is the Private Finance Initiative? · What will PFI mean for me? · Is this project me? · How to bid for a PFI project · Negotiating the contract · Delivering the service and generating the revenue · Long-term issues · Lessons learned · Speculation for the future · Bibliography · Appendix

ISBN: 0 7277 2662 5
Price: £35
Page Extent: 92 pages
Size: 297x210mm
Cover: Paperbound
Publication Date: April 1998

Available from Thomas Telford Publishing

Customer Service Department, Thomas Telford Publishing, 1 Heron Quay, London E14 4JD
Tel: 020 7665 2464
Fax: 020 7537 3631
Email: orders@ice.org.uk or via the Internet at www.t-telford.com